MEDIA MANUALS

The Small Television Studio

MEDIA MANUALS

The Small Television Studio

Equipment and Facilities

Alan Bermingham,
Michael Talbot-Smith,
John Symons,
Ken Angold-Stephens

Focal Press
London & Boston

Focal Press
is an imprint of the Butterworth Group
which has principal offices in
London, Boston, Durban, Singapore, Sydney, Toronto, Wellington

First published 1975
  Reprinted 1979, 1983, 1985

© The authors, 1975

ISBN 0 240 50869 6

Printed and bound in Great Britain by A. Wheaton & Co. Ltd, Exeter

Contents

Introduction

The applications and opportunities for the TV camera grow daily. Equipment and techniques that not so long ago were the prerogative of the professional broadcaster have been adapted to suit the needs of the educator, the advertiser, the industrialist, and many others outside the entertainment industry.

Here we are going to look at the features and amenities that typify the small TV studio, with a total area of around 150 sq. metres (1600 sq. ft.) or less. Such studios represent the most effective unit-size for many small-station applications. We study, therefore, the equipment and facilities required, their functions, and the general standards that have proved necessary for daily productional use. We shall meet the various operational aspects of TV production that come together in the studio. TV is itself a highly technical medium, but we do not need to master its engineering complexities to use studio amenities successfully.

Most closed circuit TV users aim, within their budget, to achieve the highest possible standards. This means that the studio installation has to be very carefully planned — with sufficient inbuilt flexibility to anticipate any possible future expansion. Major structural work and ventilation systems, for example, are expensive items to modify afterwards.

Equipping a studio can be a costly business; and there is always the temptation to use low-price, or secondhand professional equipment to make the budget go further. However, there are hazards. Equipment made to a lower price is less likely to be rugged enough to maintain performance under long-period heavy-duty use. Older, used facilities may be an excellent buy but could prove less reliable. Spares for obsolescent units may not be readily available. Current production techniques may not be practicable with outmoded systems.

In the TV studio many diverse skills come together to build the resultant production (their various techniques are covered more fully in other *Media Manuals.*) But an appropriate and co-ordinated studio system is necessary for the provision of opportunities for efficient teamwork. In this outline of the small TV studio's needs, we can see the facilities framework from which creative production springs.

ACKNOWLEDGEMENT
The Authors would like to thank the Director of Engineering of the BBC for permission to publish this book.

Studio: Initial Planning

Here are some questions which need to be answered at the initial planning stage.

The studio's function
What is the function of the studio, what types of production are envisaged and, most important, how much money is there available for the project?

The possible size of the viewing audience and of the budget available depend directly on the function of the studio, whether it be university CCTV, educational TV to a widely dispersed audience, industrial training, a 'professional' small TV studio producing inserts to a large TV network, medical teaching, producing television commercials etc.

The types of production to be mounted affect the studio area (see page 18) and the facilities required.

What turn-round time is required between productions? A quick turn-round requires more staff and/or greater flexibility from the studio facilities to meet changing production requirements.

Will the studio operations be in monochrome or colour? Generally, monochrome is simpler and cheaper to install and operate than colour (page 12).

Remote productions
Are all the programmes to be carried out in the studio? If location work is required e.g. on-the-job training, this could be covered either by a film crew or by using a mobile control room. The mobile control room could also be used for the studio productions on a 'drive-in' basis i.e. it could be parked adjacent to the studio, and the camera cables, microphone cables etc, would be run from it to the studio.

This may be a solution to the problem of trying to mount studio and location productions on a limited budget.

Constructional considerations
Where should the studio be located? If it is to be part of a school or university, it must be adjacent to the 'consumer', unless the studio is to feed a large number of consumers by radio or cable links. If there is a free choice of location, 'man-made' hazards for sound insulation should be avoided—motorways, railways, airports. Local high powered radio transmitters can also cause interference problems.

Will the studio be purpose built or, be in a converted existing building? Suitable buildings in the correct location are not easy to find. The main factor to bear in mind is the height required in the studio (see page 18).

Finally—what about future expansion? The philosophy should be optimistic—try to see where possible expansions may take place—extra studio area, new studio, change to colour working etc.

TYPICAL STUDIO PLANNING CONSIDERATIONS

GENERAL

INTENDED FUNCTION OF STUDIO
COMPLEX

- PRODUCTION PURPOSE—
  Educational, Industrial training, Medical
    teaching, etc.
  Package programmes, Commercials, etc.

TYPE OF PRODUCTION

- Interview, presentational (linking), utility
  (general use), demonstrational, complex
  presentation, etc.

NUMBER OF STUDIOS

- EXTENT AND FREQUENCY OF USE—
  Multi-use, rate of throughput, Scale of
    facilities required.

BUILDING LOCATION

- Accessibility, environmental intrusion.

TYPE OF BUILDING

- ADAPTED
- EXTENSION
- CUSTOM BUILT

STUDIO

DIMENSIONS

- FLOOR AREA/SHAPE
- HEIGHT

CAMERA TYPES

- MONOCHROME, COLOUR
- STANDARDS — Broadcast, Educational,
  CCTV.
- LENSES

LIGHTING

- CAMERA SENSITIVITY, Studio
  ventilation.
- LUMINAIRES—Number, size, types,
  accessories.
- SUPPLIES—No. of outlets, dimmers,
  console/control facilities.
- LAMP MOUNTINGS—Suspension
  systems.

OPERATIONAL CONTROL COMPLEX

- FIXED—Communal, segregated rooms.
- MOBILE FACILITIES—Drive-in unit,
  Location units.

VISION FACILITIES

- VISION MIXER/SWITCHER
- VISION CONTROL

SOUND FACILITIES

- SOUND CONSOLE—extent, flexibility.

RECORDING FACILITIES

- PICTURE—Videotape, Film, Editing.
- SOUND—Magnetic tape.

ANCILLARY SERVICES

TECHNICAL SERVICING

- Mechanical, Electrical, Electronic
  workshops.

STORAGE FACILITIES

- SCENIC AND TECHNICAL EQUIPMENT

ARTISTES' SERVICES

- Make-up, Wardrobe, Dressing Rooms, etc.

SCENIC SERVICES

- Scenic construction, assembly, storage, hire.

FILM SERVICES

- Own film units, or hire; processing; editing.

Colour Requirements

What are the implications of deciding to operate in colour? Technical equipment is generally more complex and more expensive compared with monochrome equipment.

Equipment for colour
Colour cameras have to produce three video signals (red, green and blue).
The three colour signals are usually *coded* immediately:
1. To avoid the need for three identical transmission links to the viewer.
2. To produce a suitable compatible signal which can be used by the monochrome viewer as well as the colour viewer.
The vision mixer also has to be colour capable. This involves extra processing of the vision signal. Vision amplifiers have to have a better, more precise specification than for monochrome.

Colour monitors are more complex than monochrome, and require a more involved adjustment. The circuitry is more intricate, incorporating a decoder to retrieve the correct red, green and blue signals from the coded signal.

Recording equipment has to be more sophisticated to ensure the correct replay of the recorded colour signal. Telecine machines are complicated, to the same extent as the studio cameras. Colour film is more expensive to purchase and process than monochrome.

Lighting for colour
A higher lighting level is required, approximately three times that required for monochrome (using identical types of pick-up tube). The colour of the light (colour quality) is critical—the light sources cannot be dimmed over a wide range, without introducing colour distortion—particularly on faces.

The ventilation system should be capable of handling the extra heat generated by increased lighting. Extra time is required for the line-up adjustments of the studio equipment.

Technical staff who have to operate and maintain colour equipment need to have adequate colour training so that they have the necessary specialised knowledge. They will expect a correspondingly bigger reward.

Colour operations require very close liaison between the staff involved in realising the visual output of the studio—costume, lighting, make-up, scenic design, graphics etc. Colour problems arising during studio rehearsal leave little time for correction.

So in view of all this—is it worth it? In many cases the answer is 'yes!' Colour adds an important extra dimension to the production, realism is easier to achieve (if that is required) and there is greater opportunity for finesse, and higher audience appeal.

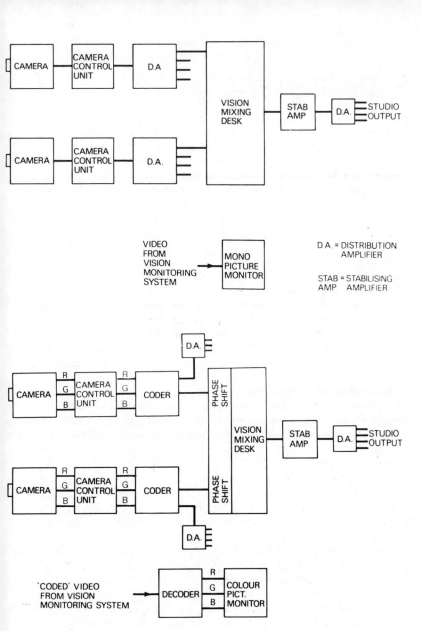

COMPONENTS OF A TV STUDIO
Monochrome TV Studio
Here we see in outline, the component parts of a two-camera monochrome TV studio vision chain.

Colour TV Studio
A colour system necessarily involves more extensive and more complex equipment, as this basic outline of a two-camera vision chain in a colour television studio shows.

13

Facilities determine productional opportunity.

Basic Studio Facilities

The size of the studio and the scale and type of production, determine our precise requirements. However, at the upper end of our survey (the studio of 150m²) there is a need for comprehensive facilities. These can be categorised as technical and production.

1. Technical — vision facilities (including lighting)
             — sound facilities (including talkback)
2. Production — scenic design (including graphic design)
              — costume
              — make-up

Technical facilities

Technical facilites are usually permanent features within a studio and its associated environs, and do not change on a day-to-day basis.

The upper illustration opposite shows the possible vision and sound sources for a production. The various 'boxes' we see here are examined in detail in later pages.

Production requirements

Production requirements, on the other hand, change from one programme to the next. In order to meet typical production requirements, the various functions shown in the lower illustration are needed.

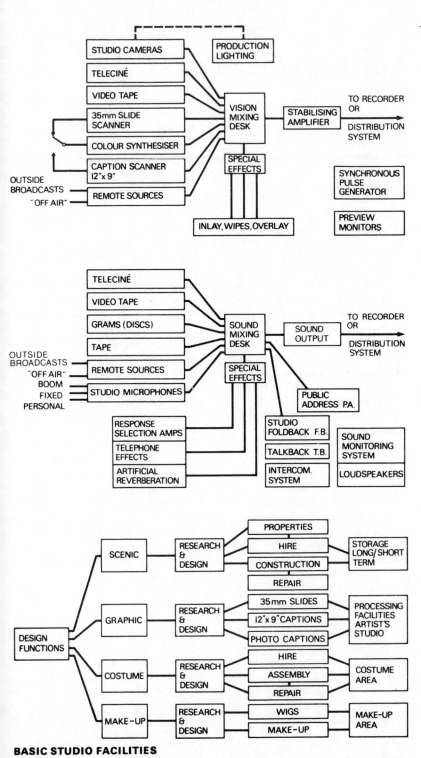

BASIC STUDIO FACILITIES

15

Layout of Control Areas

The three main control areas associated with the TV studios are:
1. Production control, where the director and his immediate production staff are located.
2. Vision control area, where the lighting director and video engineers/operators are located.
3. Sound control area, where the sound mixer audio control specialist and his staff are located.

Location near the studio
The control areas need to be adjacent to the studio and have easy access to it. It is desirable also, to have a large observation window which overlooks the studio floor. This enables the control room staff to see what is happening in the studio (provided the window is unobstructed by scenery or the cyclorama).

For colour TV studios, the observation window should be treated with a special blue colour-corrected coating. This enables direct comparison to be made between the colour picture monitors and the studio scene. Occasions arise where studio lighting spills into the control room, and we need a form of venetian blind over the observation window to prevent this stray light diluting the pictures on the monitor screens.

Communal control area
With a small studio all three control areas may be in the same control room. This has the advantage of economy on the number of picture monitors and loudspeakers required. It also allows easy communication between control room staff. But it has the disadvantage of a greater likelihood of possible high mutual interference. The audio control specialist (sound supervisor) usually prefers to operate with a high loudspeaker volume. This enables him to listen for any low level interference which may be present on the studio's sound output (e.g. hum, ventilator noise, talkback induction). To avoid the need for compromise, the layout shown at (b) is recommended.

Separate control areas
The third basic arrangement, is usually adopted in larger studios. It has the advantage that it completely isolates the functions, so that the staff can concentrate more easily on their particular tasks. However, a comprehensive communication system and many more monitors and loudspeakers are required in this layout.

Finally, equipment which generates excessive noise and heat should be excluded e.g. telecine and videotape machines should have a separate area, as should the lighting dimmers controlling the studio lamps.

CONTROL ROOMS

A Combined control room

The videotape and telecine area may be included in an adjacent soundproofed room which has an observation window into the main control room.

KEY:
1. Sound mixer.
2. Vision Supervisor.
3. Director.
4. Producer's assistant.
5. Technical manager.
6. Tape & Grams operator.
7. Vision mixer.
8. Lighting director.
9. Vision operator.

 Window

 Monitor

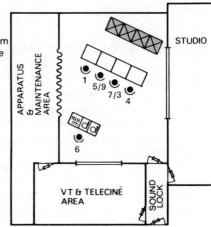

A

B Separate sound control

The sound control room should have a raised floor to enable the sound staff to see the monitors in the production control room. Separation facilitates sound operation without distracting production staff.

Window

Monitor

B

C Multi control complex

Here the various functions have been separated: production control, vision, sound. However, although this overcomes mutual intrusion (noise, instructions), it can lead to looser coordination.

Window

 Monitor

C

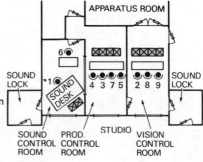

Studio Construction

The studio has to provide an environment that allows all operations to be carried out in reasonable comfort and absolute safety. Factors to be considered when designing a studio or when looking for a suitable building to convert into a studio are as follows:

Area and shape
The area required depends on the use for which the studio is intended. The relative sizes of studios and their uses are shown opposite.

The proportions of the studio (width : length) are important for the larger studio if the maximum utilisation of the available area is to be achieved and cameras/booms are to cover the area easily. It should be within the range of 1 : 1.1 to 1 : 1.5; preferably close to 1 : 1.3. A 1 : 1 ratio is undesirable because it can give rise to unsatisfactory acoustics.

The structural height required is often a neglected factor, particularly when existing buildings are converted into small TV studios. The minimum height required can be determined by considering:
1. Height of the cyclorama cloth or scenery needed to avoid shooting-off.
2. Suspension system required for the lighting equipment.
3. Space occupied by ventilation systems (trunking, outlets).

Floor, walls and ceiling
Except for situations in which the camera is absolutely static, the studio floor should be horizontal, level and firm to prevent vibration. A tolerance of 1·6mm displacement in 3m should be satisfactory for all but fast moving camera dollies. A solid floor base is essential. It should be quiet to walk on and firm so that when cameras are moved on it there are no extraneous creaks.

The final surface of the floor should be non-slip, of matt finish, durable, and be capable of withstanding continual painting with water-paint followed by washing. Cameras cannot move smoothly over uneven floors, so many surfaces are simulated. Carpets often have to be painted on the floor, as do cobblestones, parquet floors, tiles etc. The unpainted colour of the floor is important too, especially for colour TV. It should be a light neutral (grey) colour so that light reflected from it does not throw a colour cast on the performers' face.

The studio walls should be as thick as possible to provide good sound insulation, and shoud be acoustically treated to control reverberation time and sound quality in the studio. Ideally the only windows should be special windows into control rooms.

The ceiling should be strong and thick to provide good sound insulation and to support the lighting and scenic suspension system. For new installations it is desirable to build the studio itself independently from its foundations to the roof and so prevent structure-borne noises from reaching the studio (see page 24).

TYPICAL PRODUCTION REQUIREMENTS		
AREA	STUDIO FUNCTION	NUMBER OF CAMERAS
10m² -15m²	PRESENTATION NEWS ("TALKING HEAD" TO CAMERA)	1
30 m²	STATIC 2 WAY INTERVIEWS SIMPLE DOCUMENTARY PRESENTATIONS	2
60m²	MULTIPLE INTERVIEWS SIMPLE LIGHT ENTERTAINMENT, DOCUMENTARY, & EDUCATIONAL.	2/3
150m²	THE SMALL TV STUDIO INTERVIEWS, QUIZZES, SIMPLE L.E. DOCUMENTARY, & EDUCATIONAL SMALL SCALE DRAMA	2/3

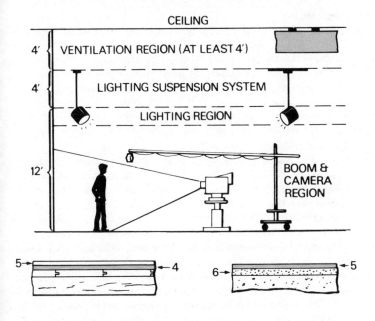

SPACE AND FLOORING
Typical space allocation
A studio should have sufficient height to accommodate various installation services, such as ventilation, lighting suspension. Each tends to use a defined region of the studio space.

Studio flooring
An existing wooden floor may be stiffened by using large sheets of 1" plywood (4). The plywood should be screwed every 2" to the existing floorboards.
In this well-constructed floor, heavy duty linoleum (5) has been laid on carefully levelled asphalt (6) on a concrete foundation.

Too easily overlooked or taken for granted.

Studio General Services

In addition to the sound, vision, and lighting facilities equipment, the studio needs to have various features to facilitate efficient production.

Access
Ideally the studio should be at ground level, to allow easy access for scenery, 'props' and technical equipment, which may range from grand pianos, and motor vehicles to animals of various sizes.

Studio doors should be large, thick and heavy to provide easy access and to prevent loss of sound insulation. Smaller lightweight sound-trap doors, are usually provided in addition to the larger heavy doors for ease of use by actors and studio staff (see page 23).

Power and lighting
The power requirements of production lighting in the studio are covered on page 84. In addition, the studio needs standard mains supplies to power studio equipment such as monitors, microphone amplifiers and any electrical equipment used in a particular production. A 13 amp ring-main supply is needed with outlets spaced around the studio walls (at 4m intervals, say). If it is anticipated that productions will include higher power equipment for demonstrations (e.g. machinery, cookers) then suitable power outlets (30 amp, or even 3-phase supplies) should be provided.

Cable ducts or runways leading supplies into the studio, can inadvertently provide a path for external, structure-borne sounds. A 1 or 2cm gap in the cable duct provides a cure, but a flexible earth link must be connected across the gap to ensure earth continuity.

Most studios need a supply of gas, hot and cold water, and a drainage system for such applications as cookery, chemistry experiments etc, and staging effects (pools, water displays, domestic situations).

A compressed air feed to the studio is also very useful.

The TV studio must be effectively lit when the production lighting is not in use, to facilitate such studio activities as erecting scenery, preparing equipment etc. These house lights should be able to be switched both in the studio and at the lighting console.

An emergency lighting system is also essential and usually includes illuminated exit signs' which automatically change over to battery supplies if there is a mains failure.

Studio markings and floor plans
To assist the accurate positioning of scenery, the studio walls should be marked boldly at regular intervals (half-metre, or footage marks are typical). The floor can be marked similarly with very light scoring marks to produce a reference grid. For accurate production planning, scale studio floor-plans (staging plans) are essential (page 148).

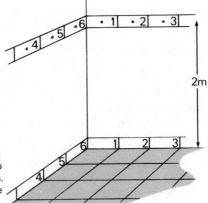

Studio floor and wall markings

The studio walls are clearly marked at $\frac{1}{2}$ metre (or 1 ft) intervals, to facilitate exact positioning of staging and equipment – to conform with the production staging plan. The floor may be lightly scored at $\frac{1}{2}$ metre intervals.

Studio distribution box

Individually identified metal-clad boxes are located at intervals along the studio walls. These contain a series of outlets and supplies for equipment.

1. Protective fender bars.
2. General production talkback pick-up points, audio tie lines, microphone points, cue lines.
3. Monitor video-feed points, and video tie lines.
4. Cue light outputs (push-button controlled in the production control room). Reverse talkback facility, prompt cut circuit.
5. Sound boom plug points.
6. Camera cable plug points.
7. Telephone to production or technical areas.
8. Distribution box identification.

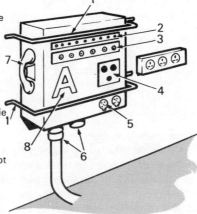

Studio Sound Insulation

A television studio should obviously be well insulated from external noise. Good sound insulation is very expensive however, so there is little point in trying to reduce levels of noise picked-up from outside the studio below the internally generated noise level (e.g. camera fan motors, ventilation, etc). A realistic studio background noise, from noise entirely originating outside the studio, is probably in the region of 30 dBA (roughly 30 dB above the average ear's hearing threshold, assuming appropriate frequency correction).

External noise

There are two types of externally-generated noise entering a studio. First, structure-borne sound is vibration conveyed through the fabric of the building, along water-pipes, etc. Such acoustic interference is usually very costly to cure. Good initial design of the building is often the only sure way to ensure satisfactory insulation. Where structure-borne sound is unacceptable, the only solution may be to stop the noise at source, by switching it off during recording or transmission (e.g. waterpumps). It may be possible, in some cases, to have machinery mounted on resilient supports so that less vibration is transmitted to the building structure.

The second type of noise is airborne and can often be reduced significantly by providing all studio doors with magnetic seals at their edges.

Any windows in the studio walls should be double—or even triple-glazed (at wider spacings than are normally used for thermal insulation—e.g. 150 cm, 6 in. minimum), and if this cannot be done, heavy shutters with good seals at their edges should be fitted. It is worth noting that, as a general rule, the more massive a partition, the better the insulation it provides against airborne noise, although some specially constructed lightweight multiple-skin structures can be effective.

Sound leakage

Sound can leak through very small apertures—hence the need for seals on doors and shutters—and if a studio suffers from airborne noise problems it is worthwhile examining it carefully for such leaks. In particular entry points for cable ducts, water pipes, etc. may be found to be ineffectively sealed.

Noise from ventilation

Studio ventilation systems can be a source of noise and, unless well designed, often have to be switched off during transmission. In general, a good ventilation system must have large cross-section trunking so that the air is moved relatively slowly. Bends in the trunking are of large radius to reduce turbulence and the inside walls of the trunking may be lined with sound-absorbent material.

22

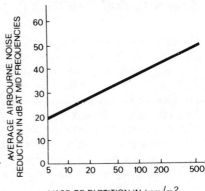

MASS OF PARTITION IN kgm/m^2

Sound insulation – structural mass
A high proportion of the external noise is airborne. Sound insulation improves as the mass of partitions (walls, floors, ceilings) is increased. Thin, flimsy structures have poor sound insulation.

Sound locks
To prevent external noises being heard when people enter the studio/control rooms, etc., small sound-absorbent cubicles are introduced, known as sound locks. Ideally, ordinary doors should never have direct access into the studio.

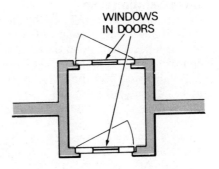

WINDOWS IN DOORS

Door seals
Doors should close as tightly as possible to prevent sound leakage. In addition to closing mechanisms (doors closers, securing levers, etc.) magnetic door seals set in plastic excluder strips, help to ensure firm sealing. 1. Magnetic strip. 2. Mild steel strip.

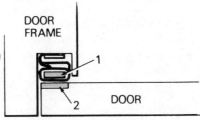

DOOR FRAME

DOOR

23

Studio Acoustics

Acoustic resonances ('standing waves') can occur as the sound reverberates to and fro between parallel non-absorbent surfaces. The character of the sound picked up by a microphone depends on where it is placed in relation to the intensity pattern of these standing waves.

Acoustical treatment

Acoustic resonances can be avoided by sound *diffusion*. This is usually achieved by introducing deliberate irregularities in the surfaces involved, so that sound waves are scattered when they are reflected.

Standing waves are not normally a serious problem in well-designed television studios, because sound absorbers on the walls reduce the reflected wave energy. Also the presence of technical equipment and scenery provides adequate scattering. However, it can happen that a set contains hard parallel surfaces, so that sound pick-up within it is poor. The best solution here is to alter the set. Opposite walls may be placed non-parallel and made of less acoustically reflecting material—e.g. canvas instead of, say, glassfibre or plywood.

Reverberation time

Reverberation time (RT) is the time taken for a sound in a studio to decay (fade away) through 60 dB. Roughly speaking, this means the time it takes a fairly loud sound to die away to inaudibility. RT is found, approximately, from the Sabine formula.

Total sound absorption is the sum of the absorption at all surfaces and is calculated from the area of the surface in square metres, multiplied by the percentage sound absorption for the surface material used.

Reverberation time affects the final quality of the sound considerably. If it is too short, speech tends to sound 'dry' (dead, unreverberant) and orchestral music lacks 'warmth' and 'blend'. Too long a reverberation time however, makes speech distant and 'echoey'.

Required reverberation times

We normally aim to make a television studio's reverberation time quite short, because reverberation can always be added artificially to the sound output, but can never be taken away.

However, it is difficult to make a studio of any appreciable size with an extremely short RT, because the floor is inevitably hard and hence non-absorbent to sound but it is practicable to make a *small* television studio with an RT of 0.3 to 0.5 seconds. This should be acceptable for almost all speech requirements and would also be quite adequate for 'pop' music, where acoustically 'dry' conditions are needed to achieve sufficient separation between the individually balanced sources.

ACOUSTIC DATA

Some Typical Reverberation Times
(at mid frequencies)

Open air	— nearly zero
Average sitting room	— 0·5 secs
Radio Talks Studio	— 0·4 secs
Theatre	— 1·0 secs
Large TV studios	— 0·7 to 1·1 secs
Concert Halls	— 1·5 to 2·2 secs
Large Gothic Cathedral	— up to 10 or 12 secs

(at low frequencies)

Percentage sound absorption at different frequencies

	60 Hz	1000 Hz	8000 Hz
Rough concrete	1	6	12
Heavy fabrics (draped)	5	80	60
Wood	5	10	15
Plain brick wall	2	4	10
Breeze blocks (unplastered)	13	65	51
Smooth plaster (painted)	1	2	2
Plaster on wood lath	7	13	13
Building board (distempered)	4	19	22
Building board with 25 mm air space	15	20	30
Glass (6 mm) plate	3	3	3

A person seated is equivalent to roughly 0·5 m² of perfect (100%) absorber.

The Sabine formula

$$RT = \frac{0 \cdot 16 \text{ (Volume in m}^3)}{\text{Total sound absorption in Sabine Units}}$$

1 Sabine unit = 1m² of 100% absorber.
If a = absorption coefficient
and s = area (m²), then
Total sound absorption = $a_1 s_1 + a_2 s_2 + \ldots \ldots$ etc.

25

Studio Ventilation

All ventilation and air conditioning systems must be considered at the early design stages of the studio complex. Not only the studio itself, but the control rooms, make-up and costume areas, tape and film storage area and technical equipment racks, all have their particular air-control requirements. The studio production lighting generates about 1 kilowatt of heat for every kilowatt of power consumed. This causes a heat build up which is not only tiring for performers and studio staff alike, but reduces their efficiency considerably.

Preventing heat build-up
Heat build up in the studio can be reduced to some extent by using:
1. Sensitive cameras, and hence lower wattage lamps for the lower light levels needed.
2. A lighting console to switch off lamps when they are not in use. A good practice is to start rehearsals with the dimmers set at half their maximum light output (often 7 on the fader), and so produce less heat.
3. A high studio ceiling so that the hot air is suspended well above the studio floor.
4. A well-planned ventilation and air conditioning system.
   The function of the ventilation system is to remove the hot air and replace it with cool dry air. The exact requirements are determined by the size of the studio and its commitments i.e. continuous or intermittent use, small sets or large sets, monochrome or colour, etc.

General problems
Problems associated with the general system are:
1. The scenery will probably not be in identical positions for each production and may sometimes obstruct low level fresh air intakes.
2. The ventilation system should be capable of changing the studio air several times an hour i.e. large volumes of air have to be moved. To reduce the noise of the air flow the ventilation ducts should be of large cross sectional area so that the rate of flow of air can be slow (see page 24). One way of overcoming the noise problem cheaply is to use a very fast (but noisy) extraction system intermittently e.g. during initial rehearsals, recording breaks, etc. Such a system should be fitted with suitable shutters to retain good sound insulation when it is not in use.

Auxiliary requirements
The studio's associated technical and production areas also require air conditioning; otherwise they will become hot and stuffy.
   Technical equipment, especially racks of thyristor dimmers, should have forced ventilation to ensure its stability and reliability.
   The power requirements of the ventilation system should be taken into account at the initial planning stage.

Basic ventilation system

If the ventilation system is to be used continuously, it should be capable of handling two thirds of the maximum lighting power in the form of heat. Use could be made of the extracted hot air for heating the studio complex. With filter (1) cooler (2) and heater (3).

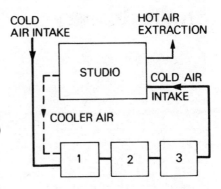

Ventilation trunks

Method of introducing cold air over the top of the scenery by means of large diameter trunks (5).

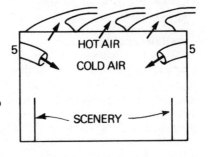

Ventilation shelves

Simple method for introducing cold air and extraction of the hot air by means of two ventilation shelves (6) which extend along the length of the studio.

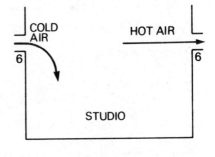

Intermittent usage

Ventilation system for intermittent use (not during transmission or recording). Heavy duty extraction fans (7). Shuttered air vents (8).

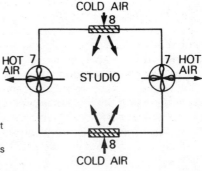

27

Studio Scenery

The type and extent of scenery (staging) required depends on the scale and forms of production envisaged, and on available budgets. There are, however, several basic staging considerations that affect studio design. If the scenery is not sufficiently high, cameras are liable to shoot over it and reveal the studio beyond. To avoid this, the cameras' shots would have to be restricted. For a 150m² studio, scenery 3m (10ft.) high should be adequate for most situations. With smaller studios and fairly static situations, less height should suffice.

For studios on limited budgets, a carefully chosen assortment of stock items can provide useful economies. The paint, like all staging materials must be fireproof and the range of colours used should be selected to provide good tonal variety in monochrome pictures.

Classifying colour
The Munsell system of colour classification can prove useful in determining the colour of paint to use to obtain adequate contrast on the monochrome picture. Colours with the same *luminance value* (brightness) on the Munsell colour charts, appear approximately the same shade of grey in a monochrome picture provided the camera's colour response is similar to that of the eye. Colours that have the same luminance value as the face (about 6 on the Munsell Scale) should be avoided, especially in situations where the scenery and the artist are lit with the same luminaire, or faces and backgrounds may merge.

Surface treatment
For small, relatively static set-ups, the scenery may often be reduced to a number of decorated sheets of flats which can be clipped to a rail. These can be changed easily and so avoid over-familiarity.

Hard-faced curved scenery should be used with caution—it can cause acoustical problems for sound pick-up.

Floor, when seen in shot, can be specially treated with washable paints. In colour studios care must be taken in choosing a fairly neutral finish, unless a special effect is required. Light reflected from a coloured floor can cause colour casts on the artists. Where floors are to painted with designs simulating parquet floors, tiles, etc, special machines incorporating large, rollers, can be used to provide rapid, effective patterns.

Scenic storage and repair
A scenery store with good access to the studio is essential. Otherwise it can become necessary to move spare scenery around the studio just in order to make working floor space available. It should have adequate height to allow the scenery to be stored *vertically*.

A workshop area is normally needed for scenic construction, repair and painting. It should be well ventilated, and acoustically isolated from the studio.

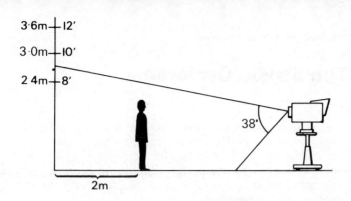

SURFACE	% REFLECTIVITY	MUNSELL NEUTRAL VALUE	TV SCALE
	100	10	
POLISHED SILVER WHITE NYLON SHIRTS	90		
WHITE CARTRIDGE PAPER CHROME PLATE	80	9	
	70		
WHITE CLOTH — — — — — — — — — — — —	60	8 — — PEAK WHITE	
NEWSPAPER	50		
	40	7	LIGHT GREY
EUROPEAN FACES ↕ LIGHT OAK WOOD GREEN LEAVES CONCRETE	30	6	
DARK SKIN ↕	20	5	MED. GREY
BLONDE HAIR DARK OAK WOOD	10	4	
DARK HAIR		3	DARK GREY
BLACK PAPER — — — — — — — — — — — —	3	2 — — BLACK LEVEL	
BLACK CLOTH	1%	0	
BLACK VELVET	0·4%		

LIMITATIONS ON SCENERY
Scenic height
Scenery needs to be about 3 m high if Long Shots are required, otherwise the camera will shoot off.

Reflectivity scale
Table relating the inherent scene reflectivities and the Munsell Scale. This illustrates the problem of working with camera tubes which have a restricted acceptable contrast ratio (30:1). A 20:1 contrast ratio inherent in the scene allows for extra contrast (modelling) added by lighting treatment.

29

The most adaptable of all scenery.

The Studio Cyclorama

The cyclorama (cyc) provides a general purpose background. It can be used as a neutral or decorative staging facility, and introduced to create the illusion of space. It is usually in the form of a large taut "cloth" which is suspended around the edge of the acting area. It is made of fireproofed duck, canvas or filled gauze and should be free of blemishes and, if possible, seam-free.

The height of the cyclorama is determined by the height of the studio and the type of production. For a 150m² studio a suitable height for the cyc would be about 3·7m (12ft.), but if production requirements are for long, wide-angle shots and/or low angle shots, a higher cyc may be necessary. The cyc can be suspended by means of tapes tied at 0·3m (1ft.) intervals to a scaffold pole suspension system, or by means of hooks on to runners using a special heavy duty curtain track.

The mobile cyc
The second method is more expensive but does offer more flexibility in that the cyc can be moved easily. Also on the occasions when the cyc is not required it can be drawn together and conveniently stored on its rail in the studio. If double tracks are fitted, different coloured cloths can be quickly inter-changed.

The cyc can either be allowed to hang freely in folds or, as is more usual, stretched taut. This is done by rolling up the spare cloth at the foot of the cyc and weighting it with stage weights or a suitably heavy scaffold pole, or by inserting a scaffold pole into a hemmed "pocket" along the foot of the cyc.

Cyc colour
The colour of the cyc is most important. In monochrome studios black, dark blue and light blue or grey are used. The last are most popular because they can be lit to give a wide range of tones. The dark blue cyc has some advantages in light entertainment productions where certain lighting effects are used. In colour TV studios, black or "white" cycs are used. The "white" cyc should reflect approximately 60% of the incident light. The light-toned cyclorama is quite versatile, for it can be lit to any chosen colour by placing colour filters over the luminaires. With suitable four-colour lighting units colour mixing over a wide range of hues and saturations can be achieved.

Care and storage
Great care should be taken if the cyc is removed from the studio. Avoid dampness—it produces stains. It should preferably be stored hanging up, not folded, because creases are difficult to remove when next the cyc is used. Even when the material is stretched taut, they persist for long periods.

30

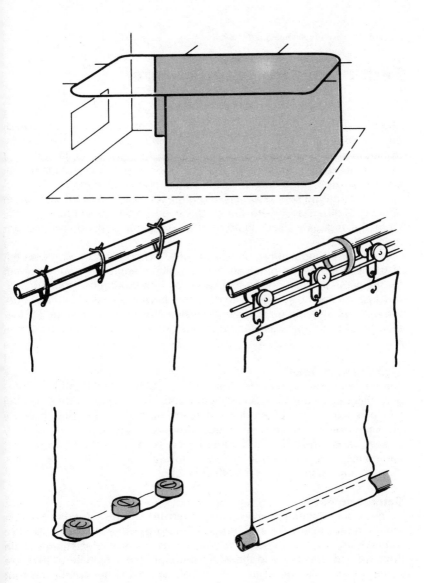

CYCLORAMAS
The cyclorama cloth
The acting area must *not* be completely enclosed by the cyc. A clear 'exit' must be left for easy evacuation of the studio. The radius of the corners should be at least 1.6 m (5 ft).

Cyc suspension
The cloth may simply be tied on to a scaffold pole, or may be suspended from a heavy duty curtain track.

Stretching the cyc
Two methods for stretching the cyc cloth: by stage weights holding surplus cloth taut; by a tubular scaffold pole – perhaps in a sleeve.

A place for everything, and everything in its place.

Technical Equipment Store

Much of the technical equipment in a television studio is not required for every production. Studios are extremely busy places. Scenery needs to be erected, lamps are rigged in their required positions, floors need to be painted etc. Equipment left around in the studio constitutes a hazard for the rigging crews, wastes space and is itself at risk. Storage space outside the setting area is, therefore, essential. A room with large doors and direct access to the studio is desirable, so that it can also store the regularly used equipment i.e. cameras and booms, picture monitors etc.

If a large enough storeroom is available, it is good practice at the end of the working day to move all the operational equipment not required for the same production the following day into this room, storing it in a tidy fashion and covering it with dust sheets where possible. In addition to the mobile studio equipment, provision should also be made for the storage of such items as isolating transformers, cue lights and caption stands.

Lighting equipment
Lighting equipment presents a particular problem. Most lighting fittings and their accessories are bulky, heavy and cumbersome. Some can be left in readiness in the studio, but many others will be interchanged between the store and the studio for every production. A mobile storage rack should therefore be provided, with supporting rails for the luminaires, and with some provision for carrying sundry accessories (flags, colour medium holders, effects etc).

Camera cables
Camera cables should always be coiled in a figure-of-eight fashion when stored on the floor, in order to avoid twisting the cable. Unfortunately, this wastes considerable floor space. It is useful, therefore, to have cable drums fitted to the walls, preferably on a spindle so that the camera cables can be wound on and off quickly. Other cables such as lighting and mains extension leads should be coiled up and stored on wall hooks. If it is not possible to provide individual hooks for the cables, each should be linen-taped together to avoid mutual entanglement.

General storage
Drawers and cupboards are useful for the general storage of smaller items. It is not, however, advisable to keep delicate or expensive equipment such as microphones in utility storage. Instead special precautions should be taken for their security and to protect them from accidental damage.

32

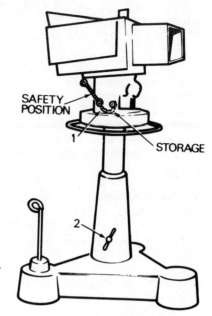

SAFETY
POSITION

1

STORAGE

Pedestal safety
Where equipment is fitted with safety locks, these should be locked before storage. A safety chain (1) on the camera head locks the tilting mechanism. A hook or turn-lock (2) may prevent column movement.

Cable storage
Camera cables should be stored in a figure of eight-pattern with dust covers fitted on both ends. Power and video cables should be stored on drums and wall hooks. (Discarded videotape spools make useful supports for storage of short cables.)

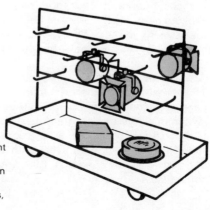

Storage trolley
A trolley should be available for movement of small items of equipment. Lighting equipment is more conveniently moved on a specially designed wheeled rack containing hooks for supporting the lights, and a tray for accessories.

Make-up

The make-up required by performers varies from such remedial aid as lightening an obtrusive beard line or removing the shine from a bald head, to full character make-up which may involve ageing, scars, wigs and so on.

A room set aside specifically for make-up is desirable, even in the smallest installations. This room should be adjacent to the studio and be well lit and ventilated.

Typical facilities

A successful layout may include two make-up positions in a room. Each should have a washable working surface, with ample leg room beneath it. A large mirror should be provided at each position, with suitable lighting of the subject's features. Peripheral lighting around the mirror is usually effective, augmented perhaps by angled fittings. Particularly where character make-up is involved, the chair supplied should be comfortable and fitted with a head-rest, together with a foot-rest or rail under the table.

The room should also be provided with suitable hand-basins, hair-sprays and associated hair-styling facilities, as hair-work is an essential aspect of the make-up artist's skills. Sufficient power sockets should be included for equipment such as hair dryers, tongs, rollers, shavers and so on, and temporary adaptors avoided where possible. Cupboards should contain material for all make-up requirements, including a range of pansticks, pancakes and conventional female cosmetics, as well as such preparations as shampoos, lacquers, and colouring agents. Further accessories include tissues, cotton wool, soap, cleansing agents and astringents.

Storage

Storage may be required for items of stock not in regular use, such as artificial blood and black tooth enamel. Small television studios are unlikely to carry stocks of wigs, beards and other specialised appendages, these being hired when required. Finally, hanging space should be provided for clothes, make-up gowns, etc.

Amenities

To keep abreast of the production, both performers and make-up staff need a monitor connected to the studio output and a loudspeaker switchable between programme output and studio talkback.

A well-equipped make-up room not only enables the make-up specialists to work effectively with the precision that their job entails, but provides surroundings that staff and performers alike will find congenial.

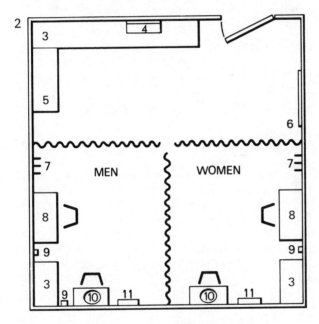

MAKE-UP FACILITIES
Make-up position
This typical make-up position (1) combines well-lit working conditions for the make-up artist, with comfort for the performer.

Basic make-up/changing room layout
Where space is limited, effective organisation is essential. Here sliding partitions or curtains sub-divide the area (2). 3. Storage cupboards. 4. Picture monitor and speaker. 5. Wardrobe (closet). 6. Mirror. 7. Clothes hooks. 8. Make-up position. 9. Power supplies (shavers, driers, etc.). 10. Wash basin (with mirror and strip light). 11. Towels.

35

Costume

The facilities required for costume or wardrobe purposes can vary considerably, according to the types of production being handled. The minimum is a partitioned changing-room, where male and female performers can dress or change costumes. This changing-room should be adjacent to the studio and the make-up service rooms, to enable quick costume changes or repairs to be made without unduly delaying rehearsals. It should be equipped with such fittings as hangers, a shoe rack, long mirrors, etc. Where productions contain a number of performers, a further area (a 'green room') may be desirable, in which they can relax between calls (so avoiding overcrowding other accommodation), but ensuring that they are readily available.

Typical amenities
Costume staff can require several types of amenity, for their services may include the preparation and provision of costumes (clothing may be personal or hired), dressing performers, and providing emergency facilities (e.g. substitutes for unsuitable clothing, running repairs, etc.). Wardrobe services can involve workrooms, storage areas, and studio service areas. For smaller studios, these may be minimal.

Costume suitability
Costume can appear unsatisfactory on camera for a number of reasons. White shirts are a regular problem, owing to the limited contrast-handling capabilities of the television system (page 42). Exposure for good facial modelling makes such shirts appear blank white. Exposure for detail in the shirt, makes the face appear unduly dark. It is as well, therefore, to keep a range of suitable off-white shirts for replacement purposes.

Clothing may prove unsuitable on camera for technical or artistic reasons, e.g. it is too dark, appears translucent, or has close patterns producing distracting strobing effects. A well organised wardrobe aims to provide an acceptable substitute. Where chroma-key (colour separation overlay) is used in a production (page 72), no clothing should be of similar hue to the switching colour—e.g. blue—or spurious effects arise. So, again, costume substitutes should be available.

Studio area facilities
Studio area facilities may be as simple or as comprehensive as we choose to make them. Basic clothes pressing and refurbishing are a routine requirement, as are repairs, cleaning and laundering. Where materials (shirts, blouses, table coverings, etc.), prove over-light on camera, they may need 'dipping', i.e. being lightly dyed to a blue or coffee hue to reduce 'blocking-off' (crushing out). Where quick-service treatment is impracticable, the materials will have to be replaced.

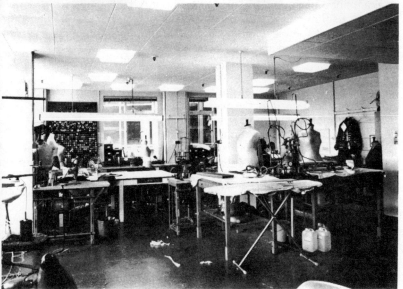

WARDROBE REQUIREMENTS
Stockroom
Part of the stock-room servicing a large television station. Available space is normally restricted, so that only regularly required or adaptable wardrobe is generally retained, other articles being hired.

Workroom
A workroom necessarily associated with a large stockroom to enable alterations to be made to stock costumes, and to reduce the range of sizes that would otherwise need to be kept.

Equipment Maintenance Area

Although strictly speaking, maintenance is of several distinct types (mechanical, electrical, electronic, plant, etc.) a single general-purpose equipment servicing area is a must for the small TV studio.

The room set aside for equipment maintenance should be situated close to the studio. It should have doors wide enough to permit access of bulky studio equipment, and windows, if any, fitted with blinds.

Laminated plastic working surface should be at a convenient height for an engineer to work either standing or seated at a stool. Double power outlets are normally provided spaced a maximum of a metre (three feet) apart along the front and rear of the bench. Additional outlets carrying the studio low voltage supplies are also required and sound and vision tie-lines from the studio carrying pulses, test signals and patchable spares are essential.

Storage

Maintenance engineers are renowned hoarders of things which 'could come in useful' and rapidly fill all the available space. A compromise has to be made between leg-room for the comfort of the technician and drawer and cupboard space.

Lighting

In addition to conventional fluorescent room lighting there should be fluorescent lighting directly over the working surfaces together with adjustable table lamps. Every studio has its dark, almost inaccessible corners, and an inspection lamp or a torch can prove very useful.

A set of small drawers with labelled compartments for the storage of spares such as fuses, indicator lamps, nuts and bolts and electrical components is desirable so that they may be quickly located. Cables are usually stored on wall hooks. Also required are tool-boxes containing essential small tools including screwdrivers, pliers, side-cutters, wire strippers, soldering equipment, Allen keys, spanners, trimming tools, etc. Larger tools may be kept in a drawer, though a preferred system, because it enables an easy visual check to be kept on the tools, is to hang them on a wall panel. Each tool here is allocated a hook or clip against a full size silhouette of the tool painted behind it. The bench should be fitted with a good quality vice.

In the electronic field, two pieces of measuring equipment are essential: a precision oscilloscope (preferably with high-gain and dual-beam plug-in amplifiers) and a multi-meter. A second multi-meter is useful for occasions when two simultaneous measurements are required. For precision camera alignment, such items as a cold-light illuminator, transparency and associated test charts and a light meter should be available.

Finally, a filing cabinet for manuals, technical literature and fault records sould be provided.

TYPICAL STUDIO MAINTENANCE ROOM

This general purpose maintenance room provides regular servicing facilities (electrical, electronic, mechanical) for the small studio. It may be supported by a central (base) maintenance group dealing with more radical problems.

Furnishings include: (1) Plastic-topped heavy-duty bench, (2) vari-height stool with back support, (3) storage cupboards/drawers, (4) small component drawers, (5) document filing cabinet, (6) adjustable wall lamp, (7) extensive power points.

Tools include: (8) large items on storage rack, (9) comprehensive portable tool kit, (10) oscilloscope, (11) multimeter, (12) soldering iron with heat-shield stand.

Safety in the Studio

Safety is a very personal matter—the behaviour of the individual affects everyone. Safety does not come about naturally. It is the result of anticipation, care and sensible regulations. It is a good policy to have someone specifically responsible for safety. Some studio hazards are detailed here, but always watch for others as well.

Fire
This is a major subject in itself and the advice of the local fire authority is recommended when considering the many factors involved. All studios must comply with the local building regulations.

Large studios have a fire lane about one metre wide around the studio perimeter. This is a non-acting area and no equipment or scenery is allowed to remain in it. It provides unobstructed access to the studio exits. In the smaller studios this may not be entirely practical because of space lost, but there must always be unobstructed access to two exits. Any actual fire used in the studio should be stringently supervised, with fire-fighting apparatus at the ready.

Electrical
Special safety regulations have to be observed if more than one phase of the mains supply is present in the studio. This is because a high voltage exists (415v for a 250v supply) between any two phases—and this can be *lethal*! All metalwork associated with electrical equipment should be earthed (grounded). All electrical equipment should be fitted with a correctly wired 3 core mains lead. Often domestic electrical equipment and musical instruments are fitted with a 2 wire mains lead. An isolating transformer should be used with such equipment.

Luminaires should be tightly clamped to the lighting suspension system, and must be fitted with wire safety bonds. All accessories too (e.g. barndoors), must be safety bonded to the luminaire.

Tripping accidents
The most common trip is over cables on the floor. All main access 'lanes' to the studio exits should have portable cable ramps over them.

Lifting
Staff with back troubles abound in television studios. All staff should be given adequate training on how to lift correctly. If possible staff should be given first aid training including artificial resuscitation.

Unstable items
It is all too easy to rest a ladder against a wall, inadequately support a scenic flat, raise a heavy lamp high on an unweighted lighting stand. But the unguarded moment will come, when the unstable hazard falls—pulled by a cable perhaps—and then it is too late too think about SAFETY!

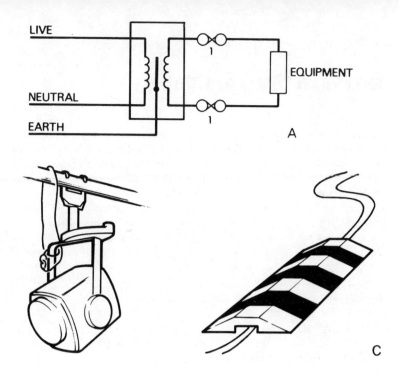

A

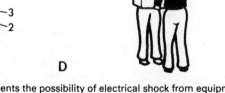

B

C

D

SAFETY

A. Isolating transformer

The isolating transformer prevents the possibility of electrical shock from equipment-to-earth contact. Its case and electrostatic screen must be earthed. The secondary winding must not be earthed, and have correctly rated fuses (1) in each leg.

B. Safety bonds

Wire safety bonds should be fitted to all suspended and overhead equipment. Luminaires and their attachments are bonded as we see here.

C. Cable-ramp

This typical cable-ramp (cover) in wood or glass-fibre (e.g. a metre, 3 ft 6 in long) protects cables and prevents trip-over accidents.

D. Weight handling

Get into the habit of lifting objects safely. (2) Knees bent, (3) palm grip (not just fingers), (4) chin in, (5) straight back, (6) elbows in.
If the object is heavy, get assistance.

Each type of pick-up tube has its distinct characteristics.

Choice of Camera Tube

A television camera is similar in principle to a standard photographic camera; it differs by using a pick-up tube (in place of film emulsion) to convert the image of the studio scene into an electrical signal.

Tube types
Only three types of TV camera pick-up tube are currently in use: the Image Orthicon (obsolescent), the Vidicon and the Plumbicon.

The pick-up tube is located in the camera head, behind the lens system. In the Vidicon and Plumbicon tubes the optical image of the studio scene is focused on the tube target. This comprises a transparent, conductive signal plate on which a photo-conducting layer is deposited. Light variations in the focused image produce a corresponding electrical charge pattern on the latter, which is scanned systematically by the tube's electron beam. The entire TV system, from camera to receiver, is synchronised by special 'sync' pulses. The result, is the video (picture) signal.

Relative merits
The main advantage of the Vidicon is that it is small, relatively cheap, robust, easy to adjust to achieve good pictures. It has good sensitivity and resolution, is widely used in portable black and white cameras, telecine and caption scanners. This tube is used universally in closed circuit television systems. Vidicons are usually operated with a fixed lens aperture (stop) and the target voltage varied to obtain the correct level of electrical picture information.

Its disadvantage is that under low light levels (less than 100ft/candles) picture smearing is noticeable if the camera pans or the subject moves quickly; also a comet or trailing effect is seen on moving highlights.

The Plumbicon tube is considerably more expensive than its Vidicon counterpart; it is similar in construction and retains all the advantages of the Vidicon. However, it has certain important advantages of its own. It is much less susceptible to smearing at low light levels, and considerably more sensitive than the Vidicon (up to three times). Its disadvantages are that earlier Plumbicons were slightly red insensitive and that electronic correction is needed to overcome a lack of sharpness (definition).

The Plumbicon operates with a fixed target voltage (usually 20 volts) and the lens aperture is adjusted to obtain the correct level of picture signal.

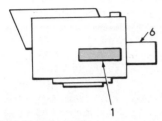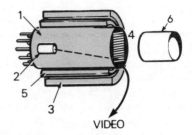

THE CAMERA TUBE

The camera tube (1) located within the camera head, behind the lens system (6) generates a video signal from the image focused upon it.

A stream of electrons from the electron gun (2), is focused by a surrounding coil (3) to a fine spot, which scans the target (4) in a series of lines (e.g. 625, 525 overall), controlled by a further coil (5). This systematic scanning builds up the electrical video (picture) signal for a complete picture every 1/25th sec. (Europe) or 1/30th sec. (USA).

Tube Types	I.O.	Vidicon	Plumbicon
Incident light needed.	3″ 300-350 Lux 4½″ 500-600 Lux	1″ 1200-1600 Lux ⅔″ 50-600 Lux	Monochrome: ~ 500 Lux Colour: ~ 1600 Lux
Lens stop	f5·6	f2·8 & f2·0	f4·0 & f2·8
Tube size	4½″; 3″	1″ & ⅔″	1¼″ and 1″
Contrast Handling	20:1	50:1	30:1
Comments	Virtually obsolete. Difficult to line up for for optimum results.	Easy to line up. Smears on low Light levels and 'Trails' on highlights target approx. 30 volts but varied as operational control.	Slightly red insensitive. Needs electrical compensation (aperture correction to improve sharpness. Fixed target, iris varied to produce correct video output. Universally used in colour cameras.

Camera Lenses

The function of the camera lens is to collect light from the studio scene and to focus it on the photo sensitive surface of the pick-up tube; it is made from high quality glasses mounted in a metal tube. It must transmit (or pass) as much light as possible with the minimum amount of optical distortion. To control the amount of light reaching the pick-up tube the lens system is fitted with a variable aperture in the form of an iris mechanism. The aperture is calibrated in "f" numbers.

Lens manufacturers identify lenses by their focal length but for television production planning it is more convenient to refer to a lens by its horizontal angle of view. A lens with a short focal length has a wider angle of view than a lens of larger focal length.

Fixed focal-length lens

A fixed-focal length lens can be screwed into the body of the camera directly in front of the pick-up tube and offer a single fixed angle of view. Such a system is employed on cheaper equipment, or where a camera is used for only one fixed job (e.g. scanning captions). Alternatively, a set of three or four such fixed lenses (with different angles) may be attached to a rotatable turret at the front of the camera head.

Zoom lens

The development of the zoom lens is reaching the stage where most TV and cine cameras are supplied with this form of lens. The principal advantage of the zoom lens is that it offers a *continuously variable* angle of view between two fixed limits. Typical horizontal angles are 6° to 30° (a 5:1 zoom) and 5° to 50° (a 10:1 zoom). The latter range (10:1) is best suited for studio operations.

The zoom is usually controlled by two handles clipped on to panning handles at the rear of the camera; the right-hand control is used for changing the angle of view and the left-hand one for focusing.

The zoom may be directly operated mechanically, or electrically by a servo-control mechanism. The latter provides a smoother control action.

Certain zoom lens designs have the facility for fitting range-extenders. With this facility, the intrinsic ratio remains the same (say 10:1) but the actual angular range available alters, e.g. from a 5° to 50° coverage to 2½° to 25° coverage by fitting a x2 range-extender. However, the f number is doubled and any defects magnified by a factor of 2.

Cheaper zooms suffer from several disadvantages, including poorer resolution and uneven performance. Their restricted minimum focusing distance too can be a frustration during production. While more complex, expensive zoom systems can be sharply focussed on objects half a metre from the camera (e.g. twenty inches), a simpler zoom lens may only focus down to two metres.

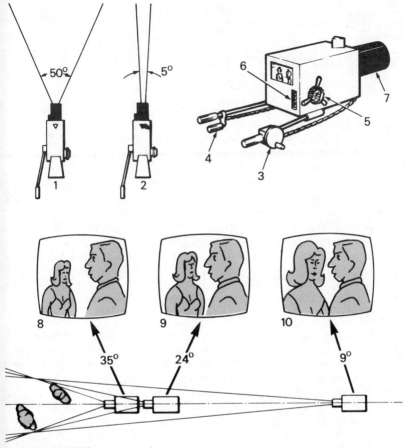

CAMERA LENSES
Lens angle
The lens angle is determined by the focal length of the lens we use. With a 1 in camera tube, a 15 mm lens (1) will cover an angle of 50°, while a 150 mm (2) lens (ten times as long) covers 5° (1/10th of the original angle), making the subject appear ten times as large.

Setting up the zoom lens
Zoom in on distance object (turn 3 fully clockwise). Focus zoom (4). Zoom out (turn 3 fully anti-clockwise). Check tube focus (5). Repeat all above three times, and lock off tube focus (5). In operation, zoom in 3, focus 4. Zoom out as required.
3. Zoom control.
4. Zoom lens focus.
5. Camera tube focus.
6. Pre-selected angles (shot box), only on servo systems.
7. Zoom lens.
If servo controls are fitted 3 and 4 are *reversed*.

Perspective and the lens
For a given size of foreground, perspective will alter as we change the lens angle. Wide angle lenses (8) appear to exaggerate distance and perspective, while narrow angle lenses compress space (10).
Depth of field increases as the lens angle widens, but the image produced is proportionally smaller (at a given subject to camera distance).

Camera Mountings

A standard television camera is normally too large and heavy for hand-held operation. Recent developments in professional colour camera design have reduced typical weights to under 20lb. To provide a firm, rigid support for the TV camera, a mounting of some kind is invariably used. The actual type used depends largely on the type of production. Most TV productions require the camera mountings to be wheeled smoothly around the studio and, preferably, to provide adjustable camera height (elevation).

The television camera-head itself is fixed to a *panning head* which in turn is bolted onto a camera mounting. The panning head is deliberately designed to have a certain amount of (adjustable) friction to steady the camera and facilitate smoother, more controlled panning and tilting. Various types of camera mounting are in current use, the ones described here being operated by a single cameraman.

Tripod

This is a three-legged stand with independent adjustment of the length of each leg. Once set up, the overall height is not easily changed. The tripod is cheap and lightweight, but only allows the camera to be used in one static position. If the splayed tripod is mounted on a base with wheels (skid) a rolling tripod is obtained. The assembly can be wheeled around—but only out of vision if optimum smoothness is required.

A slightly more elaborate mounting has an adjustable central column that can be moved up and down ('elevate' and 'depress'). This allows the operator to perform limited tracking shots and also to change the height of the camera head (not "on shot") over a range of three feet to five feet from studio floor level.

Pedestal

The pedestal is a highly sophisticated, carefully engineered one-man camera mounting. It enables both subtle or marked changes in camera position and height to be made while on shot. It can be moved around the studio quickly and silently, with minimum effort, guided by a steering-ring, or a tiller-handle. The weight of camera and panning-head is counterbalanced, so enabling the cameraman to change elevation easily, with little physical effort. Beneath the pedestal's base, mechanical linkages line up its three wheels, either to point in the same direction (crab) or to enable one to steer while the others follow.

Great care must be taken, to secure (lock off) its central column before attempting to remove the camera. Similarly, the central column must never be released from its 'low' position, for it will spring up with enormous lethal force.

Other camera mountings, such as cranes and powered devices are available, but these are generally too large and unmanoeuverable for small studio use.

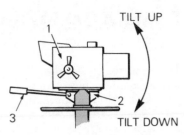

TILT UP

TILT DOWN

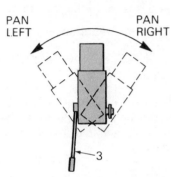

PAN LEFT · PAN RIGHT

The television camera

The *camera head* (1) is attached to its mounting by an adjustable *panning head* (2), to which a guiding *panning handle (3)* is affixed.

The camera can *tilt* vertically, and *pan* horizontally. (Independent tilt/pan locks prevent accidental movement.) The camera head can be repositioned along the panning head for optimum balance.

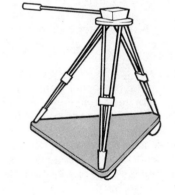

Wheeled tripod

A tripod with legs of pre-adjusted height, is fitted to a wheeled base.

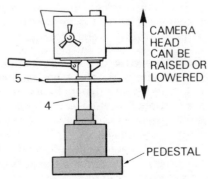

CAMERA HEAD CAN BE RAISED OR LOWERED

PEDESTAL

Pedestal

The steering ring (5) is used to raise and lower the balanced pedestal column (4). It is also used for steering the pedestal around the studio.

47

Camera Cables and Cabling Points

The camera cable is the vital link between the television camera-head and its camera control unit.

The function of the cable is twofold: to bring the picture output of the camera (the video) from the studio floor to be electronically processed and then fed to the vision mixer; and to convey supplies of various types to the camera itself.

Cable construction

The cable is a multi-way cable with a plug at one end and a socket at the other end. Both ends have a keyway to ensure that the cable locates correctly.

The different types of wire within the camera cable carry various signals and supplies, including the picture output from the camera, synchronising pulses, electrical power, talkback circuits to the camera, and specialised voltage feeds to ensure correct operation of the pick-up tube.

Cable care

If the camera cable is to be disconnected and stored, even for a few days, it is essential to fit its protective caps over each end to prevent dirt or moisture entering the socket-end or pins being bent at the plug-end. If caps are not available, cable ends should be wrapped in clean cloth and taped up.

Damage to the camera cable end or to the entry socket on a television camera may occur if the cable is clamped to the pedestal body and the camera head then elevated with insufficient slack cable.

This form of damage can also occur with a clamped camera cable if the panning head is turned continuously in one direction and the camera cable becomes snarled up around the column of the pedestal.

Similarly, a cable should not be made to follow acute bends or twists in use because, if it is subsequently pulled tight, damage to the internal wires can result.

When the pedestal plus camera are pushed away to the side of the studio for storage at the end of the studio day, the cable should be coiled up in a figure of eight configuration alongside the camera.

Cabling points

The camera cable plugs into a cabling point on the studio wall. Alternative points are generally distributed around three of the four studio walls. Some well-equipped studios have more cabling points than studio cameras. This enables each camera to route its cable to meet the production requirements of a particular programme, and so avoid long loops of straggling cable around the studio floor. A patching panel is then required to cover the possible combinations of camera couplings in the vision apparatus room.

The cable end

The camera cable is fitted with a plug at either end, housing many small pin connections (1). Take care when attaching the cable, to avoid bending pins. Also ensure that the cable is pushed fully home and screwed up firmly.

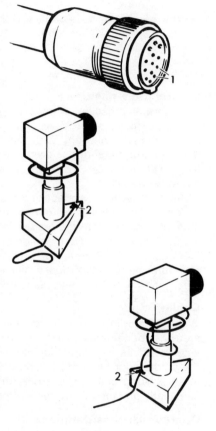

Cable care

Anticipate possible cable damage by allowing sufficient cable length for column elevation and panning movements. Cable clamps (2) are usually fitted to the camera mounting.

Cable plugging

Camera cables plug into distribution boxes located at intervals along studio walls. These sockets are permanently routed to a communal patch panel (with point locations) near the camera control units. Here, flexible cables from these units plug into their associated camera's wallpoint link.

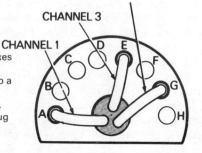

CHANNEL 2

CHANNEL 3

CHANNEL 1

Vision and Lighting Control Area

This area has two interrelated functions. Here the picture quality is continually monitored and adjusted by the vision operator, or video engineer (page 152) and here also the lighting facilities are controlled (page 98). Because these jobs require close co-ordination, the vision control desk and the lighting control panel (dimmer panel) should always be arranged side by side, preferably sharing common picture monitors. Optimum results cannot be achieved if they are located and operated in separate rooms.

Control room position

It is normal practice in smaller studio centres, where space is at a premium, to house the vision/lighting control area in a communal production control room, with the director and other programme staff. Such an arrangement has certain economies, but where space permits (page 16), a separate adjacent room with a communicating glass panel has advantages.

All the associated electronic equipment for the studio should be rack-mounted with adequate front and rear access in a room immediately adjacent to the production control area. If space is particularly restricted, this vision equipment may have to be placed in the production control area, but such an arrangement does not make for optimum servicing efficiency. Over-communal layouts can cause the different activity requirements to impinge on each other.

Cabling

Where a studio is purpose built false floors are preferred for control areas, for beneath them accessible cable ducts can house all power and video supplies. Similarly, ducting may be provided around the edges of the studio floor for camera cables, etc. If equipment has to be installed in an existing building, overhead trunking suspended from the ceiling can neatly and effectively solve difficult cabling problems.

Operational considerations

The positioning and layout of operational controls needs to be carefully considered. Equipment detail will be determined by manufacturers' design, but we should always bear in mind that operators will need to reach controls comfortably and quickly over long periods with a minimum of fatigue. There must be an uninterrupted view of all picture monitors, which should be arranged to permit both overall assessment and local scrutiny. The lighting control panel should also be conveniently located. It is often forgotten that adequate desk space is needed for productional paperwork, such as scripts, cue-sheets, lighting plots, etc.

In small studio productions, one man can handle both the studio lighting balance and operate vision controls. Larger productions require separate operators for lighting and picture control.

50

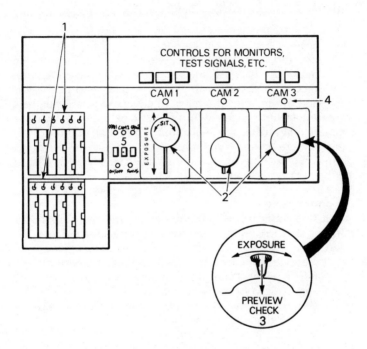

VISION AND LIGHTING CONTROL

In this small unit, dimmers and switches for the studio lighting circuits (1) and the vision controls adjusting picture quality (2) have been conjoined. The knob controlling each camera channel (3) adjusts exposure/target (up/down), sit/black-level (rotate), and compares its picture with the one being transmitted (press).

Exposure control may adjust either the *lens aperture* (iris, diaphragm), as with the plumbicon camera tube, or the *target voltage* as with the vidicon.

The desk also has controls for monitors, test signals etc., indicators for "on air" channel (4) and camera call buttons(5).

51

Camera Control Unit

We regard the camera control unit (CCU), as the electronic processing centre for each camera's pictures. Joined to its studio camera by a long, multi-way cable (the camera cable—page 48), each CCU originates and controls camera supplies, scanning waveforms, etc., as well as amplifying and correcting the video signals from the camera-tube. The process of adjusting the CCU and its associated camera for optimum performance, is known as the camera line-up (page 54).

The size and location of these electronics varies with the type of camera design. In cheaper and miniaturised TV cameras, most of this control circuitry is housed within the camera-head itself. Adjustments are made after removing a protective cover. Alternatively, the CCU may be separate from the camera, but have no external controls or it may be a separate unit and also have externally mounted controls.

The camera control units for a studio should be grouped, and mounted so that line-up can be achieved easily, with free access for separate apparatus room.

CCU connecting

Each CCU is connected to a number of points, including the studio synchronising pulse generator, talkback systems, cue (or tally) lamp information, and to the vision control desk. This last is, in fact, simply a convient operational extension for various adjustments on the CCU itself. Each camera's picture, after treatment here, is fed to the input of the vision mixing panel (video switching panel) in the production control room, where the vision mixer (switcher) selects the required source for the programme sequence (page 66).

In a colour system, the number of line-up controls is increased relative to a monochrome system. Each one of the three camera-tubes (providing red, green and blue outputs) requires separate circuitry. Additional facilities ensure the registration of their three pictures.

Automatic operation

Certain monochrome cameras have a special device for 'automatic' operation, which enables the camera to produce consistently bright pictures, even when lighting levels vary over a fairly wide range.

This has advantages in certain circumstances; especially on external locations lit by daylight, where excellent results can be obtained. However, the auto system gives poor results in scenes involving high subject or lighting contrast. It reacts to bright areas by reducing the camera's exposure and reproducing middle tones (e.g. faces) as too dark. Conversely, it responds to dark areas by reproducing these mid-tones as too bright. Exposure is arbitrarily affected by picture content. Such a system is suitable for experimental and simple training work, but is rarely satisfactory if consistent results are desired.

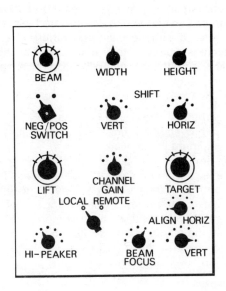

THE CAMERA CONTROL UNIT

The camera control unit contains the various electronic adjustments required for correct camera tube alignment. These are set during "camera line-up", using special geometrical charts, while examining picture and waveform monitors.

Camera channel alignment

Beam: Camera tube beam current should be sufficient to clarify off-white areas in scene (discharge whites).

Scan width and height: Adjusts scan limits on camera tube, to 4 : 3 aspect ratio.

Neg/Pos switch: TV picture positive or negative tones.

Vertical/horizontal shifts: Moves complete scanned area position (centralise).

Lift: Moves all picture tones up/down tonal scale.

Channel gain: Video signal amplification (1 volt overall).

Target: Varies tube target voltage. In vidicon used to adjust picture amplitude.

High peaker (aperture correction): Electronically enhances picture sharpness (but increases picture noise).

Beam focus: Achieves focus of the scanning beam in camera tube.

Alignment: Positions scanning beam down camera tube.

Local/Remote switch: Switches lift and target controls from CCU to a remote *vision control* position.

Line Up of Camera Channels

For optimum picture quality (sharpness, tonal gradation, colour quality and registration), a camera and its associated electronics must be selectively adjusted—the camera line-up. During rehearsals any minor picture shortcomings can be tolerated, but for the recording or transmission period, only the best will do, and a careful line-up is necessary.

Starting the day

At the beginning of the studio day remove camera covers, switch on all studio equipment, but leave the lens caps on, and allow five minutes for the electronic equipment to stabilise.

Do not spend time lining up cameras at the start of a studio day, for even highest grade equipment can 'drift' after several hours' operation. Turn up beam controls (if they are not pre-set), uncap the camera, and check that pictures of reasonable quality are available for the commencement of studio rehearsal. A more comprehensive check should take place later in the day (probably while production staff take a meal break) when the channels have 'warmed up'. Rehearsal time is too precious to interrupt it unnecessarily.

Auxiliary apparatus

A line-up chart, which contains checks for definition, geometry, tonal gradation, and electronic performance, may be in the form of a special card or a glass transparency on a 'cold light' illuminator panel similar to an X-ray print examination light. The line-up chart checks both overall and local definition (sharpness), scan size and position (to fit the aspect ratio of 4 : 3), edge definition (to ensure that detail does not deteriorate at the sides of the picture).

Manufacturers' instructions give details of the actual line-up operations. Some, like the channel gain, are quite stable, and only require an occasional adjustment. A 'clipper' is included in the circuitry so that the video signal cannot exceed a pre-set maximum.

Before starting to line up the camera channel, make sure that your picture monitor is providing a high quality picture. Point the camera straight on to the line-up chart. Check that the lens is sharply focused on it (optical focus) and set target and lift (black level) controls to their normal operating positions. (Target affects the camera's sensitivity, and alters the contrast and evenness of the picture. Lift ensures that only the darkest picture tones are reproduced as black.) Adjust beam so that the white area of the chart does not 'trail' when the camera is panned. Next set the beam focus for best definition. Scan controls altering the picture's position and size are now adjusted to just fill the rectangular area of the picture monitor.

When all the camera channels have been lined up, operational controls are switched over to the remote vision operator's position.

USING A LINE-UP CHART

Line-up (alignment) charts enable us to adjust each camera channel for optimum performance, and to ensure matching pictures between cameras. Some comprise geometric patterns and tonal steps. Others also incorporate a multi-tone "standard picture".

Features	Purpose	Adjustments	Comments
1 Border Marks	To set limits of scan to aspect ratio 4:3	Heights, width, Hor. shifts. vert.	Controls adjusted to just fill scanned area. Check by pointing channel at circle after line up.
2 Step Wedge	Checks ability of channel on contrast range.	Beam Target lift iris.	Ability to discriminate each individual tone. Set 'Beam' to just discharge on whitest step.
3 Chequer Board			Picture should not 'streak' from white into black and vice-versa.
4 Frequency Gratings	Ensures maximum definition or sharpness from channel.	Camera *optical* focus, then 'beam focus', then hi-peaker.	To check *lens* definition and channel definition at edges of picture. Use edge gratings.
Overall picture		Lift target iris.	Each studio camera pointed at chart in turn. Controls indicated adjusted so that cameras *MATCH*.

Vision Control

We sometimes forget that the TV camera can reproduce only an image of what it sees—and then only within its limitations. How good an interpretation the camera provides depends on the quality of our equipment, whether the picture is in monochrome or colour, how we use our facilities, and so on. The TV camera itself can handle only a limited range of scenic tones if it is to reproduce them effectively. Under certain conditions it introduces spurious blemishes (noise, streaking, lag, ghosts) into the reproduced picture. By careful continuous adjustment, however, the camera's electronic performance can be adapted to suit the scene before it. This process is known as vision control. Without such adjustments, we would find ourselves with a succession of pictures that were too light or too dark to be seen clearly, or shots where detail was completely lost.

Vision control functions
Vision control has several functions in the TV studio:
1. To ensure that the TV system is adjusted so that its technical performance is optimum (adjusting exposure and tonal quality to obtain a good video signal, detecting faults, etc.).
2. To provide the most effective pictorial interpretation of the studio scene created by staging (scenic) and lighting specialists. The vision control operators adjusts tonal reproduction, matches picture quality, etc., to this end.
3. To serve as liaison point for the cameramen, relative to technical problems that arise during the course of rehearsal.

Video adjustments
Watching a series of picture monitors (one for each video source), the video operator controls the electronic performance of the cameras at all times when they are actually 'on the air', and when they initially set up their shots. In this way he matches successive pictures, so that their brightness, contrast, mood, are consistent. Fortunately, the TV camera's output is instantaneous, so that results can be seen immediately, and any necessary corrections made.

Arrangements vary somewhat with the type of camera tube, but exposure (either by lens-aperture, or target voltage adjustment) and lift (sit, black level) are the main controls used. Exposure is adjusted to obtain good gradation in the most important subject tones (lightest and darkest areas may have to crush-out beyond the system's limits) and maintain similar face tones in conjoined shots. Lift moves the reproduced tonal scale upward or downward, usually to locate darkest picture tones or the video system's 'black level'. Whether vision control is carried out sitting beside the camera CCUs, or at a grouped console housing all the remote controls of all video sources, depends largely on the scale of the facilities.

PICTURE QUALITY

The picture lacks detail in lighter tones (burnt-out), while shadows reproduce as mid-grey. This may be due to:

vidicon —	High target voltage and/or lens aperture too large (overexposed) and black level being high (sat-up).
plumbicon —	Overexposed, and sat-up.

Good picture quality. Good tonal gradation throughout the important tonal range; although note that detail is lost in the sweater and hair, that is present in the subject and is visible in (3).

Dark picture overall. All picture tones reproduced at too low a value. Details lost in mid to dark tones. Typical reasons for this include:

vidicon —	Target voltage too low and/or lens aperture too small (underexposed). Black level (lift) may be set too low (sat down).
plumbicon —	Underexposed, and sat down.

PICTURE FROM CAMERA   VIDEO WAVEFORM

57

Monitoring the Vision Signal

As we saw earlier (page 42) the TV camera scans the scene and produces a fluctuating electrical signal (video) corresponding with the distribution of light and shade. From that point on, we shall find the television picture being discussed in two distinct ways. Most people are only interested in the final reconstituted picture that appears on their picture monitors or receivers (directors, make-up, wardrobe, set designer). They are not concerned with the electronics involved. But engineers and technical staff are also concerned with seeing that this video signal (with its sync pulses) from which the picture is derived, passes through the entire TV system to the viewer in an exact, undistorted form. Any changes would modify the clarity, tonal gradation (or colour) of the resulting picture. Consequently they continually inspect and measure the video on special waveform monitors or oscilloscopes (CRO). Here they see drawn out in a line of light, a 'graph' of the video fluctuations over one scanning line (or over a field) of the television picture.

The TV waveform
The television waveform comprises two parts: above the base-line the picture signal; below it, the sync pulses. These two features are measured separately. Picture levels are assigned on a scale of IRE units from 0 to 100. Sync pulses are measured on a scale from zero at the base line (blanking level) down to −40 units.

The proportions of the waveform may instead be expressed in voltages. The picture occupies a maximum of 0.7 volt and the synchronising pulses 0.3 volt. The overall level of composite video (picture plus sync information) is therefore one volt on a line of 75 ohms impedance.

The television system cannot tolerate variations of system parameters, otherwise picture faults, and disruptions (frame slip, tearing, etc.) arise. It is essential for the television signal to be accurately monitored at all stages in its progress.

Signal control
Whereas the amplitude and timing of the sync pulses should remain constant at 0.3 volt, the amplitude of the picture signal is influenced by the vision operator. He adjusts his controls as a result of viewing both the picture monitor and its waveform monitor for each channel. The latter shows him how the video relates to the system's limits, and prevents his inadvertently losing information by black-crushing or overexposure.

This interpretation must be achieved quickly, because a smooth flow of matched camera pictures is an essential ingredient to a successful television programme.

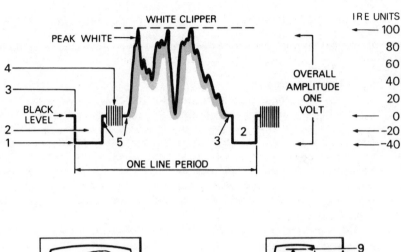

WHITE CLIPPER

PEAK WHITE

4

3

BLACK
LEVEL

2

1

5

3   2

ONE LINE PERIOD

OVERALL
AMPLITUDE
ONE
VOLT

IRE UNITS
100
80
60
40
20
0
-20
-40

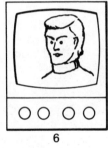

6

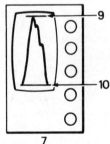

9

10

7

PICTURE CRITERIA
The video waveform
The video waveform includes picture information (coloured) together with
synchronising pulses. These are inserted in the line and field retrace (flyback) periods.
1. Synchronising level.   2. Line sync pulse.   3. Front porch.   4. Colour burst in back
porch.   5. Commencement of picture.

The television picture
The vision operator watches both his *picture monitor* (6) (for pictorial effect) and his
waveform monitor (7) (to ensure that the video waveform is within the system's limits).
The *waveform monitor* is an oscilloscope displaying the video waveform (at line and
field sweep-rates) against a calibrated graticule (IRE units), showing the peak white
level (9), and black level (10) limits (traced as reference lines on the monitor tube).

Picture Monitors

A picture monitor is, to all appearances, a high grade TV set without sound. It does not contain the circuitry for 'off air' reception, but is instead fed directly with a selected source's picture. It is the vital part in the control of camera pictures and represents the final link in the picture chain. The size of a monitor screen varies from a compact 5in. to 26in. (diagonal) for group viewing.

Monitor adjustment

An incorrectly adjusted picture monitor not only shows a misleading version of the camera's shot, but is liable to cause us to alter the staging, lighting, or picture quality inappropriately. A suit may look too dark, simply because our monitor is wrongly adjusted! Most monochrome monitors include a power switch, brightness, contrast, and picture scan controls (height and width). Switch on, and after a few minutes' warm-up time, check that the picture shape is right (4 by 3 aspect ratio). A test card containing a circular design immediately reveals geometrical distortions.

Monitor line-up is easiest where we can display a suitable line-up chart or signal with a series of gradated tonal steps. Otherwise align all monitors to a static picture containing a full tonal range. First, turn the brightness and contrast controls fully down; then turn up the brightness control until a picture raster (the basic line-structure of the picture) is just seen. Now turn up the contrast control until a well-balanced full-tone picture with no defocusing in the highlights is seen.

Where a specially generated electronic monitor line-up signal is used, adjustments of brightness and contrast can be made in a few seconds. Alternatively, a standard grey scale step wedge can be used.

All high-grade picture monitors are fitted with a black-level clamp (i.e. are fully d.c. restored) to ensure that tonal values remain constant, regardless of changes of picture content.

Colour monitors are complicated to align and their adjustment should be left to a skilled technician. Operational controls are brightness, contrast and colour saturation.

Monitor termination

To avoid distortions and loss of signal strength, a picture monitor is provided with circuitry (a 75 ohm termination) that matches it to its video source. Where more than one monitor is to be supplied from the same source, only one termination is required.

Monitor suitability

While some monitors reproduce the pictures from helical-scan video-tape recorders quite satisfactorily, others do not. Instead, the picture is unstable, and accompanied by jitter and synchronising problems. It is as well, therefore, when selecting monitors for such a system, to ensure that they will reproduce helical VTR signals effectively.

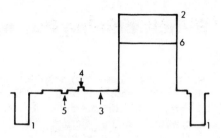

Monitor line-up signal

A multi-tone, electronically generated
signal enables us to line-up picture
monitors to a consistent standard. The
signal from this "picture line-up generating
equipment" (PLUGE) is as shown in A.
1. Line sync pulse.
2. Peak white signal (100%).
3. Overall background (0%).
4. Background tone (+3%).
5. Background (−3%).
6. Mid grey.

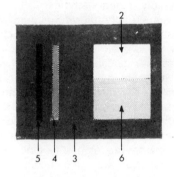

Adjusting the monitor

The monitor *contrast* control is adjusted for
the required highlight level (e.g. 25
ft/Lamberts). Adjust the *brightness* control
so that the black bar appears black, and the
dark grey bar can only just be distinguished.

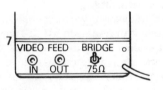

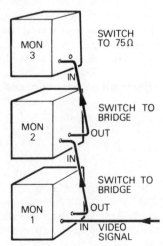

Monitor bridging

When a picture signal is to be looped
through a series of monitors, only the last in
the chain should be *terminated* (i.e. a
resistance switched across its video input).
A switch at the rear of a picture monitor
will be marked BRIDGE (or *high*) and 75Ω.
This should be positioned as in the diagram.

61

Synchronising Pulse Generators

The television picture is scanned systematically in a series of parallel lines, each picture is actually covered in two successive scanning patterns (odd and even fields) which are automatically interlaced to form a fully-scanned picture (frame).

The television pick-up tube generates the picture information on a line-by-line basis. At the end of each line the scanning spot flies back rapidly to begin the next. This continues until a complete field has been scanned, when it returns quickly to the top of the picture to commence the next field. To ensure that this scanning process is carried out with precision, and the entire TV system synchronised from camera to receiver, special 'sync pulses' are generated to initiate the line and the field scanning actions. A special *synchronising pulse generator* (SPG) produces these electronic pulses, which are added to the picture information. Any studio centre with more than one camera needs an SPG to act as a common reference point for all camera channels, telecine and caption camera chains. The SPG is the heart of the vision system—failure of this one device causes total failure of all picture sources. A back-up spare is, therefore, essential.

Picture timing

In television, we are dealing with signals that change in less than a millionth of a second! So, when a series of video signals travel over any appreciable distances by cables of different path lengths, we find that their arrival times at a given point are dissimilar. Consequently, their synchronising pulses appear time-displaced. To avoid this dilemma, all cable lengths to a vision mixing point should normally be identical, whether from cameras, telecine, slide scanners, video-tape, etc. (all are made equal to the longest). Without accurate picture timing, sideways displacement or definition loss may occur on mixes, while in colour systems a hue change could arise.

External picture sources

The various studio video sources are all synchronised by a communal SPG. But what if another source synchronised by a *different* SPG is also to be included in the programme? We cannot mix, or superimpose it upon our local sources, for the new source would not be in sync with them. We can only cut between unsynchronised sources.

One solution is to arrange for our system to be synchronised by the incoming source's pulses. This 'slaving' technique is known as genlocking. Mixing, wiping, overlaying, etc., can now be achieved.

If your SPG has no means of locking to an external picture signal ensure that your vision mixing panel has a 'non-sync' channel on at least one of its inputs, so that a 'clean' (undisturbed) vision cut between sources can take place.

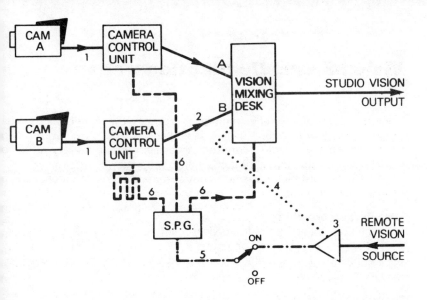

TELEVISION SYNCHRONISING PULSES

Synchronising pulse	Abbreviation	Function
Monochrome		
Line Drive	L.D.	Synchronises line-scanning process (at the end of each scanned line).
Field Drive	F.D.	Establishes field synchronisation. (Scanning beam returns to top of raster on completion of each field.)
Mixed blanking	M.B.	Picture information is suppressed by blanking pulses, to permit insertion of line and field sync pulses.
Mixed syncs	M.S.	A composite sync signal consisting of both line and field sync pulses. Required by monitors/receivers to maintain horizontal sweep synchronism during field retrace period.
Colour – additional signals required		
Colour subcarrier	S.C.	A constant frequency generated as a reference for colour information. (Added to the luminance signal to form an encoded signal for transmission.)
Reference Burst		A short burst of subcarrier frequency inserted into the back porch of line sync pulse (i.e. once per line), to ensure correct reproduced hue.

Synchronising the camera system

The synchronising pulse generator (S.P.G.) ensures that all the video sources are in exact synchronism. This avoids such problems as picture cut-off, roll-over, tearing, displacement, that would otherwise arise. Where remote picture sources are used (e.g. outside broadcast unit, remotes) their system must be synchronous with the studio if pictures are to be mixed or superimposed. In one system (genlock) sync pulses are derived from the remote source to drive the receiving studio's pulse train.

1. Camera cables. 2. Video output connections. 3. Video distribution amplifier.
4. Video feed ("remote" to mixing desk). 5. Genlock input. 6. Synchronising cables (note that all must be the same length).

Vision Signal Distribution

Once one of the available picture sources in the studio has been selected by the vision mixing desk (switching panel) in the production control room, this picture on the 'transmission' or 'studio output' channel needs to be distributed—to various monitor points in the building, to recording systems, to central routing areas (e.g. continuity, network control, etc.).

Distribution amplifier
The function of this unit is to duplicate picture signals and isolate connected apparatus. Up to six separate outputs can be obtained from certain amplifiers. The amplifier should produce 'copies' that differ in no way from the original input signal.

Termination panel
As outlined above, the studio-output picture signal must be distributed to a variety of areas, viz. video tape, telecine, lecture halls, viewing rooms, etc. This is achieved by a patching panel in the studio apparatus area, which enables picture (and sound) signals to be routed to selected points.

Cable distribution
Picture sources can be fed to monitors or video tape recorders only over relatively short lengths of video cable (e.g. up to 200 metres/yards). Long cable runs produce degradation of pictures (especially colour signals) unless special equalisation amplifiers are used en route.

Radio frequency distribution
If many monitors located at remote points from the studio centre are to be fed, a system of RF (radio frequency) distribution can be used.

In this process the picture to be distributed (a studio's output perhaps) is fed to a modulator unit, which converts the video to a radio signal, which is then routed by coaxial cable to its destination. The picture is viewed at the receiving point on a conventional television receiver. RF distribution has the main advantage that many pictures can be channelled at different frequencies along the same cable. This is a relatively expensive system to install, but one modulator can be introduced initially, and additional modulators added as required for extra channels.

Microwave links
It may be easier to install a microwave television link between two buildings if a permanent vision circuit is needed over a distance of more than one mile. Remember that in many countries prior permission of the Telecommunication Authority must be obtained for external picture distribution.

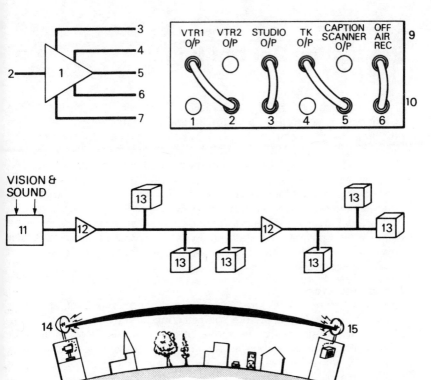

DISTRIBUTION
The distribution amplifier
The distribution amplifier (1) has zero gain and provides identical video signals at a series of isolated outputs (e.g. 3–5 points). Video input (2) can be distributed to several outputs (3–7) e.g. to: transmission monitor; floor monitor; technical director; engineering check monitor.

The termination panel
The termination panel (8) facilitates distribution of picture sources to their various destinations. Available sources are located at the top of the patch panel (9). Potential destinations (1–6) are arranged in the bottom row (10). Flexible coaxial cables or rigid U-links route the video.

Radio frequency distribution
For larger installations, the picture and sound may be fed into a *modulator* (11). The resultant modulated radio frequency carrier is distributed by coaxial cable. Distribution amplifiers (12) may be required en route to boost the signal. Television receivers are used as monitors (13).

Microwave links
Here the modulated signal is transmitted from a high point, via a parabolic microwave aerial (14). At the receiving point (15) (which must be within sight of the transmitter) the signal is demodulated (detected) and the original video and audio signals recovered.

Production Control Room

This area is the heart of any television complex. It is here that the production is controlled, and the operations directed. In this room programme and technical staff watch a series of preview monitors and the output of the vision mixing desk, which appears on the 'transmission' monitor. This is the studio output, which now passes to the distribution system for recording or transmission. The programme sound is heard over a nearby loudspeaker. Desk 'talkback microphones' pass instruction and guidance to the studio crew.

The ideal layout is still a matter of debate; in some studio centres all technical and programme staff, equipment, operate in one area. Other arrangements utilise three separate rooms for vision, sound and production control.

Picture monitors

The main features of the production control room is its bank of picture monitors previewing all picture sources contributing to the programme. Most show continuously the output of their channel (e.g. Camera 1), certain others are switched as required. The transmission monitor is centrally mounted above the preview monitors. Picture monitor layout should be just below the horizontal eye-line. The viewing distance is ideally six to eight times the viewing diagonal of the monitor screen. Nearer than that, it is tiring to continually scan around; more distant, and we lose detail.

Environment

Two levels of room lighting should be available; normal overall illumination, and localised operational lighting. The operational lighting must be arranged so that sufficient light is available to read programme scripts, floor plans, etc., with ease, and to quickly locate and operate technical equipment; extraneous light should not spill on to preview monitors. The control room should be carpeted to improve acoustics, and have effective ventilation.

Layout

Control positions for all production and technical personnel are arranged along a laminated-plastic desk (around 70 cm. high), housing such facilities as the vision mixing panel, talk back systems, remote operational controls for cameras, lighting dimmers and remote control of VTR and telecine machines.

Care spent in the design of the production desk layout will reap benefits in future productions.

Remember that additional production staff (e.g. producer, designer, wardrobe and make-up staff) *may* require access and seating; but don't allow the control room (gallery) to be an area where people can drift in and out at will during rehearsals.

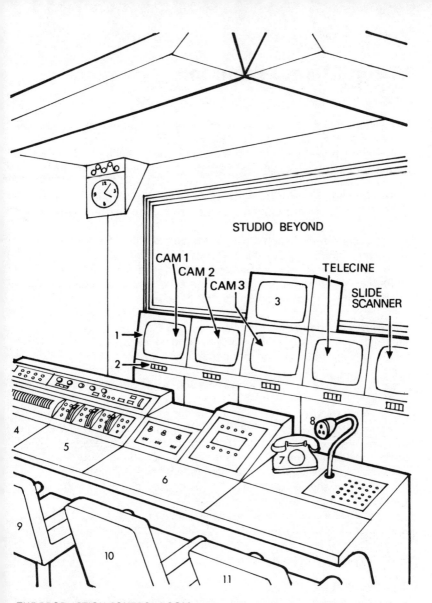

THE PRODUCTION CONTROL ROOM

In this typical small-studio set-up, we see the main operational positions overlooking the preview monitors (1) with their associated on-air lights (2) and the transmission monitor (3). Where space is limited, the sound operator may be housed here (to the left) with his equipment. The technical director (9), has the lighting controls (4), and operational camera controls (5) in front of him. The vision mixer (10) has his controls (6), and the production director (11), has communications equipment, including a telephone (7) and talk-back microphone (8).

Typical viewing conditions

Seating should not be positioned too close or too far from the picture monitors. Six to eight times the picture diagonal is preferable. Overhead lighting illuminates desk controls and scripts without spilling onto monitor screens, in the darkened room.

Vision Mixer : Function

The vision mixing desk or vision mixer is the destination point for all picture sources in the studio. The output of all the studio cameras, telecine machines, video tape recorders (when 'playing in' inserts to a programme), caption scanners (film strips and slides) are connected to the inputs of the vision mixing unit (or switcher).

The function of the desk is to edit together (by cutting, mixing, etc.,) all these various contributions to the production, as the director has planned.

The output of the vision mixing desk (studio output) is connected, via distribution amplifiers, to the transmission monitor in the production control area, and to the transmission chain, check monitors, etc., that comprise the television complex (page 64). The vision mixing desk is usually found in the production control area.

Vision mixer design

Although many designs of vision mixing desk exist, each with its own merits and limitations, the principles involved are simple enough. A flexible vision mixer should be able to cut, mix, fade up or out, superimpose, and provide effects facilities such as wipes, split screen and overlay.

All picture sources are switched at the mixer by buttons. There are two duplicated sets—on the A row (or bus) and the B row. Which row is in operation depends on the positions of the nearby faders. Pressing any of the bottom row of buttons effects a cut between sources. (The B row is the operative bank as the main faders are at the bottom.)

If we push the faders upward, a mix takes place from the source selected on B to the source selected on A.

These faders can be 'split' and used individually. If fader B is pushed upward on its own, the output of B fades to black; if fader A is pushed up and fader B left, a super (superimposition) occurs, and we see both shots transparently superimposed.

What to look for

No matter how inexpensive your system your vision mixer should fit your projected requirements. If colour facilities are planned for the future, buy a vision mixer that is colour capable.

In operation, cutting, mixing and superimposition should be accomplished without any 'break up' or 'roll' on the transmission monitor. Also the quality of the outgoing picture should be identical to that of the input picture.

Be warned! Sophisticated mixing panels do not in themselves produce better production techniques. Unskilled operation can lead to embarrassing 'on air' errors. Even when mistakes can be rectified by rerecording, this can prove time-consuming—and is often costly.

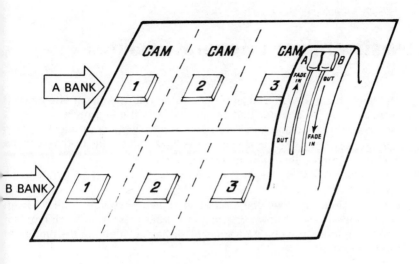

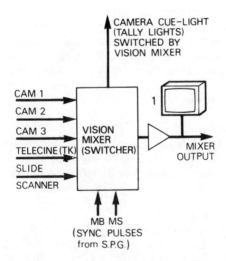

CAMERA CUE–LIGHT
(TALLY LIGHTS)
SWITCHED BY
VISION MIXER

VISION MIXING
Basic vision mixing panel

Each picture source (channel) connects with a numbered button on a "bank" of push-switches. On pushing a button (which then lights) that source is switched on to the main studio output (seen on the Master Monitor). Inter-source switching can be carried out on either identical bank of push-switches.

A pair of faders enables us to mix between sources selected on the respective banks. Thus, select A1 and B2, and downward movement of both faders produces a mix from Cam 1 to Cam 2.

Operating a fader independently (split faders) produces a fade-up or fade-out of the channel selected on that bank.

Typical vision mixer connections

To the left, various picture sources are plugged into the mixer.

Below, the required sync pulses and blanking (see page 62) are fed into the mixer.

The output of the mixer (right) is fed to Master Control (for transmission) or videotape for recording. The transmission monitor (1) shows the selected source(s).

As sources are switched, the respective cue-lamps light to show selection.

Vision Mixer : General Facilities

The sophisticated vision mixing panel offers all the visual effects (and more!) to the TV director that are available in the film-making process (on an editing machine and in the film processing laboratories). Effects that require time, skill, and costly auxiliary equipment in film, can be achieved in TV at the touch of a button.

The cut
Even the simplest mixer can cut between picture sources. The cut is an instantaneous switch from one picture to another. As with all types of transition, there must be no frame-roll or flash evident on the picture at the moment of cutting.

The mix
Here the transition is less pronounced. As the faders are operated the established picture (e.g. camera 2) fades away, while the new picture (e.g. telecine) progressively appears. Both picture sources appear on the screen simultaneously. Obviously the speed of the mix is dictated by the production requirement. A mix can take several seconds or can be almost instantaneous.

The Fade up/fade out
Half of the 'split fader' is used. A selected channel can be faded up or down (in or out), by moving the bus fader (A or B) up or down. In more complex mixers, each channel has its individual fader. Fades are normally used as introductory or concluding changes.

The superimposition
By fading up two or more picture sources together, we obtain a superimposition. This device may be used to add titling to an existing picture, or special montage effects.

Preview facilities
Certain mixers have a separate preview bank (preview bus), the video output is connected to an associated monitor. This enables us to check any selected non-studio picture source (e.g. a remote) before switching it to the transmission channel. It assists too, in preparing a combination picture (of two or more cameras' shots).

As it is operated, the vision mixing desk also switches corresponding cue lights (tally lights) on the cameras to denote which is 'on air' (for cameramen, floor manager, artists, etc.).

Practice varies as to who operates the vision mixing desk. It may be a specialist operator (the switcher or vision mixer) or the technical director; in small studios and in outside broadcast units the director may operate the vision mixing panel himself.

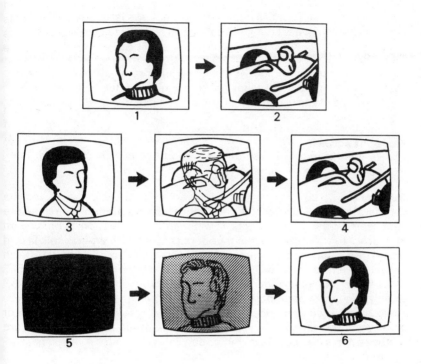

CHANGING SCENES
The cut
An instantaneous change, achieved by pressing the cut-button of the second channel.
e.g. *From* Cam 1 (1) *To* Telecine (2).
The *cut* is used when action in the two scenes is consecutive.

The mix
The first picture (3) fades in intensity the second picture simultaneously strengthening
to full intensity (4). (Holding the controls midway produces *superimpositions*.)
Achieved by fading between the banks; different sources having been selected on their
respective banks. (e.g. Cam 2 on Bank A to Telecine on Bank B.) The *mix* usually
signifies a lapse of time.

Fade up
The screen is black (5), the picture gradually strengthens to full intensity (6). The
required channel is selected on one bank, but the associated half of the dual fader is
faded out (split fader). As the fader is operated, the picture appears. Moving the control
to "out", the picture fades away.

71

Vision Mixer : Special Effects

The use of special facilities on vision mixing desks is an area of growing interest. These have recently become available in small studio centres.

The wipe
This is the most common of the special effects and can be easily described as one picture 'chasing' the original picture off the screen. The direction of entry can be horizontal, vertical, diagonal, circular, diamond shaped, and so on.

The split screen
This is a wipe that is frozen at any pre-determined point. Part of one picture is inlaid into another.

Overlay
This facility, known more fully as brightness separation overlay, has long been used for 'trick effects' in monochrome television. Wherever a tone *other* than black appears in front of the 'master camera', this is inserted into a 'background camera', replacing that part of its shot. (Alternatively, white overlay can be used.) Thus, white lettering on a black caption card could be 'punched into' a scene from another source, more cleanly than by superimposition. Similarly, a person before a black drop could be inserted and appear 'within' another scene. Inserted lettering or subjects appear *solid,* unlike the transparent effect superimposition achieves. This is obtained by a special electronic switch that is automatically actuated by a selected tone.

Black edge facility
A difficulty whenever we need titling over a multi-tone scene is that whatever lettering tone we choose, somewhere it will probably be identical with its background — and so disappear! This can be partly resolved by the addition of a thin black edge around the white lettering; this is added artificially by an electronic black edge generator.

Colour separation overlay
This is an extremely important colour TV technique for combining the outputs of two picture sources. Its application is invaluable for a studio with a small working area. Its method of operation is very similar to the monochromatic overlay system only now, instead of a switching tone, a *colour* is used to switch between sources.

The foreground camera is pointed at our subject against a blue backing (a blue cloth or a white backing lit with blue light). The switching signal is derived from the blue backing of the foreground camera, and the subject (its blue backing suppressed) is electronically combined with the background camera. Obviously, the subject must not wear or reflect anything blue, or random switching will occur.

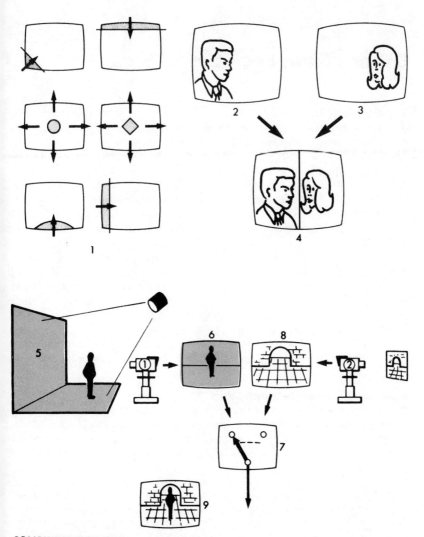

COMBINING PICTURES
Wipes
Speed of wipe is set by rate at which wipe fader is moved on effects unit. All wipe pattern directions can be reversed. Typical patterns are shown here (1).

Split screen
By stopping a wipe pattern at an intermediate position, we achieve a screen that is bisected (split-screen) or an inserted area.
Here the pictures from two sources (2 & 3) have been combined in a split-screen (4) using a horizontal wipe.

Chroma key
The subject stands before a blue backing (5). Its camera output (Camera 1) (6) is fed to the chroma key switch (7). Wherever blue appears in this shot, the switch operates and presents the background scene on Camera 2, instead (8). The combined composite shot shows the subject within the background scene (9).

73

Other Vision Facilities

Studio monitors

Television picture monitors (page 60) are used on the studio floor so that operational and programme staff (linkmen, announcers, etc.) can see a picture, for cueing or continuity purposes, of the studio output or a selected video source.

A studio monitor can be mounted on a shelf within scenery, but greater mobility is achieved if it is mounted on a trolley.

If the monitor is slung from the lighting grid or studio ceiling, it must be suspended with the same safety provisions as the studio lighting equipment.

The floor monitor can be connected to a switchable feed of any picture source available on the vision mixer. This facility is an asset where a studio commentator is linking telecine or video tape inserts. These machines have a run up time of at least five seconds and a floor monitor coupled directly to the machine enables the commentator to time his words exactly to the film or video tape insert.

The presence of a picture monitor near the studio action can be a disadvantage if performers are distracted or watch themselves and play to the camera.

Electronic character generator

A relatively new facility available in the studio is a device which electronically generates letters and numerals that can be inlayed anywhere in the picture area. The output is connected directly to the vision mixer as a normal picture source and can be processed in an identical manner.

The device consists of a standard typewriter keyboard and an associated black box which contains the character generator electronics, and may include a memory file system. The picture output appears on a monitor as white characters on a black background.

The operator watches a picture monitor, which displays an electronic marker, to locate written information in the correct position in the frame. The more complex broadcast generators have extensive memory systems which can be programmed, and their messages recalled at the touch of a button.

Off-air receiver

This receiver picks up regular picture and sound transmissions. It can be a monitor unit with a television tuner and facilities for aerial connection, or a standard TV receiver producing standard video and audio outputs connection (1 volt picture, zero level sound).

Typical applications for such a receiver include permitted off-air recording of educational material from national networks, for transmitted programme checks, and sometimes to derive test signals (staircase, test cards) from radiated tests.

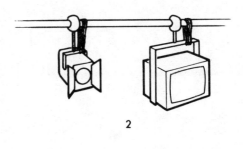

OTHER VISION FACILITIES
Studio monitors

The studio floor monitor (1) is firmly attached to a wheeled trolley for use anywhere in the studio. Video and mains cables can be wound round brackets at the rear of the trolley for storage.

Monitors fitted with a suitable suspension stirrup can be hung from a lighting grid or barrel, thus keeping the studio floor clear. Wire safety bonds secure the attached equipment (2).

Electronic character generator

Using a standard typewriter keyboard (3), the operator produces electronically generated characters which appear on his monitor screens. The display screen shows the characters alone (4) enabling the layout to be adjusted (position changes, errors cancelled).

The preview screen shows positioning accuracy when superimposed on a selected shot (5).

The display may be stored (magnetically or punched paper tape) at (6), and totally recalled as required.

Television Prompters

Prompting during a TV production may be necessary to aid recall during a memory lapse (a forgotten line), as an aide-memoire in the form of a list of the subjects to be covered, and finally, the complete text (unlearned) to be read to camera as if delivered spontaneously.

Some studios have the facility for the floor manager or sound mixer to cut the studio sound while an audible prompt is being made. Where videotape editing is a facility, this type of prompting is rarely used, because a corrected re-take of the appropriate shots is usually possible.

Prompt card

The aide-memoire type of prompting, is generally met in a current affairs or educational production. In its simplest form it may be a large card held up by the floor manager or his assistant as near to the presenter's eye-line as possible. It may simply consist of a list of topics as a reminder to the presenter.

Hearing aid

A more sophisticated communications aid, enabling the director to speak directly to the speaker (the chairman, anchor-man, presenter) fits him with an unobtrusive deaf-aid earpiece. Switch-operated, this allows the director to pass cues, up-to-date information, etc., to assist the speaker, even when he is on the air, unheard by the microphone or others in the studio. It should naturally be used sparingly and considerately, and never while the presenter is speaking or about to speak.

Roller prompter

A type of prompter that contains the complete production text, takes several forms. The simplest is a large-type paper roller, running at a speed remotely controlled by the speaker or an operator. This may be located above or beneath the camera. Instead of direct viewing, a 45° semi-reflecting mirror attachment over the camera lens can provide a reflected image of the roller. To the TV viewer, it now looks as if the speaker (who is looking towards the lens as he reads) is addressing him directly. A special lightweight TV monitor may replace the paper roll. Now the script can be typed quite normally, on a paper roll a few inches wide. This roll is shot by a small industrial camera — its televised image appearing on the prompter picture tube. If necessary, film or videotape may also be displayed on the prompter tube, together with a superimposed script, in order to ensure exact timing. The eye movements of the speaker are hardly detectable as he reads the script. The equipment is ideally suited to prepared statements, speeches, and even news situations. Last minute alterations are possible by simply cutting out redundant passages with scissors and joining on additions with clear adhesive tape, or, for small changes, sticking a blank piece of paper over the script and writing in the alterations.

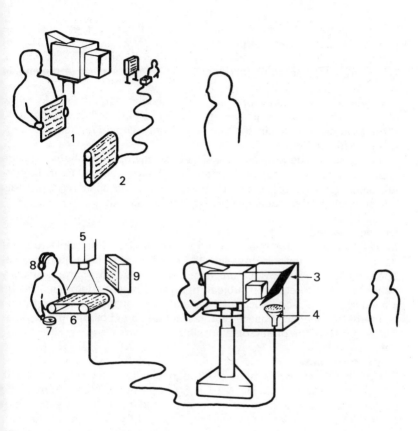

PROMPTERS
Simple prompters
A simple prompt card (1) may be held up by the floor manager for subject prompts.
A remotely-controlled paper roller (2) can display the whole script. (Mounted on floor,
stand, or on camera.)

Electronic prompter
The performer reads an image of the script (3), reflected from a prompter picture
tube (4) attached to the studio camera. This image is produced by a special prompter
camera (5) which is televising the script typed on a roll of paper (6). An operator
controls its speed (7) to suit the performer's reading rate, checking dialogue on his
headphones (8) with the display (9).

77

The rear-projected image becomes a convincing 'environment'.

Back Projection

Pictures projected onto the rear of a translucent screen positioned behind the action can be an effective way of achieving an illusion of location that is difficult or expensive to achieve directly in the studio. The picture may be static (using a 3 x 2½in. glass slide) or moving, in which case standard 35mm. film is employed.

A typical application is to simulate the view through the rear window of a car. The perspectives on the projected film and the foreground should match, and ideally the 'driver's' actions should relate to the projected road conditions.

The special slide projector consists basically of a lamphouse, a slide carrier and conventional lens system. The heat generated by its powerful xenon lamp is prevented from damaging the slide by a dichroic mirror, while further cooling is provided by a jet of air.

Moving projection

Moving projectors for this application are similar in principle to standard cinema projectors. However, the need for high light output, quiet operation and a steady picture (since the projected image is usually behind a static foreground subject) impose stringent equipment-design considerations. A sophisticated means of film transport and registration is, therefore, needed together with adequate sound blimping. No variation of speed of the projector is possible.

Projection screen

The projection screen is made of a tough, cleanable, translucent plastic which is stretched and laced to a rigid, portable, metal frame. The screen transmits about 60% of the incident light. Greater light transmission is likely to increase the visibility of a 'hot spot' in the centre of the screen. To achieve maximum picture contrast foreground lighting should be kept off the screen as much as possible. In order to economise on studio space it is common practice to deflect the projector beam with a mirror, folding its light-path.

Space problems

The mirror size required depends on the final picture size and its position in relation to the projector. The mirror is usually made from ¼-inch polished plate glass supported on a rigid mobile frame.

Back projection equipment can provide storage problems, but it has the advantage over electronic picture insertion methods, that we can see the projected image in the studio, and small adjustments may be made to performers' positions without difficulty.

In a small studio, however, back projection may prove to be unsuitable owing to the studio space required. In that case, front projection (page 80) or overlay (page 72) may be considered as alternatives.

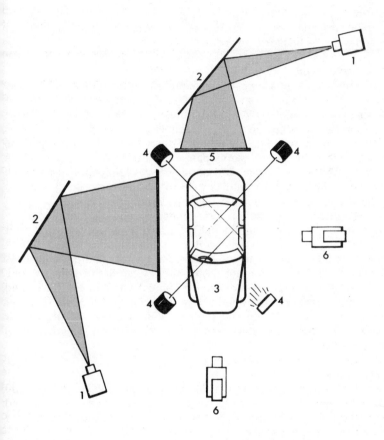

BACK PROJECTION
Here two projectors (1) have been used to suggest locations outside the car's windows. Mirrors (2) provide a more compact set-up. The perspective, lighting and quality of the projected backgrounds should match the foreground subject (3). Foreground lighting (4) should not fall upon the projection screens (5) or their images will be diluted (greyed out) and appear unconvincing on camera (6).

Axial Front Projection

Axial front projection (reflex projection) provides a method for projecting still or moving pictures, so that our foreground subject appears integrated with the background scene.

Projection set-up

The screen is made of a special plastic material covered with millions of tiny glass beads that reflect about 90% of the incident light straight back to its source. For optimum brightness, therefore, the background image should be projected along the camera lens-axis, which in turn should be at right angles to the screen. Otherwise the image brightness falls, and edge-shadow problems can arise. The high efficiency of this type of screen allows a standard domestic slide projector to be used. Thus, very little projected light is thrown on the foreground subjects and the studio lighting effectively swamps what little there is.

In a practical arrangement a semi-reflecting mirror is mounted at 45 degrees in front of the camera lens. The projector is positioned at right angles to the camera lens axis so that the image, is reflected via the mirror on to the screen. The subject and its background image can be seen directly by the camera lens, only slightly dimmed by the mirror's absorption. The camera will not see the subject's shadow on the screen if the camera viewpoint has been correctly aligned.

Apart from a loss of contrast the picture is relatively unaffected by ambient light levels, so that reasonably flexible foreground lighting arrangements are possible.

Applications

The most common use for axial front projection is to provide background scenes in almost static studio situations (e.g. behind newscasters). In this context it is ideally suited to small studios, since it utilises very little floor space.

Another use is in the realm of special effects, the enormous field of visual deception involving models, perspective distortion and all manner of trickery generally more associated with film techniques. Setting up can be time consuming and, therefore, may be uneconomic in a television studio.

The inherent disadvantages of this method are the drastically reduced mobility of the camera, and the inability of studio personnel (other than those near the camera), to see the picture.

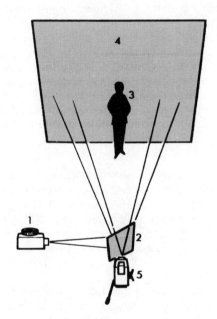

AXIAL FRONT PROJECTION
The image is displayed from the projector (1) through the 50/50 mirror (2) onto a
special beaded screen (4). The subject (3) appears located within the projected scene.
The projected image should slightly exceed the field of view of the camera (5), and the
relative perspective and proportion should match.

The well-chosen graphic enriches the television presentation.

Captions

An often neglected but important sphere of television design is that of captions (graphics). They may be moving or static, studio captions or slides, photographs (preferable not glossy), hand painted, printed with rub-on lettering, or even electronically generated.

Correct aspect ratio
Captions should conform to the television screen format (i.e. an aspect ratio of 4:3) and the design should leave an adequate border to allow for receivers that cut off a percentage of the transmitted picture. A size found convenient in most television studios is 300 x 225mm (approx. 12 x 9 in.). Captions with an incorrect shape may cause framing difficulties unless the director is prepared to accept black edges to the picture, or framing only part of the design.

Large pictorial captions can offer productional opportunities, however, even when a different format, if the script allows exploratory camera shots, or a series of close-ups.

Titling
Titles and credits are usually made with white lettering on a black background for greatest clarity; either when shown individually or when superimposed on another picture. Cutting the lettering into the background picture by means of overlay (page 72) produces clearly defined captions. A further development is to feed the output of the caption camera into a black-edge generator (page 72).

Colour synthesiser
In a colour TV system, to avoid the necessity of producing expensive coloured captions the colour synthesiser has been devised. The equipment accepts monochrome captions from which it generates coloured captions. The hue and saturation of the lettering and background may be varied over a wide range.

Moving captions
Captions can include a certain amount of movement or change. Very sophisticated works of 'cardboard engineering' can be devised for complicated illustrations. Rolling captions are normally achieved by printing the information onto a black paper roll which is conveyed between two rollers either manually or by a variable-speed electric motor.

Electronic characters
Electronic character generators are a useful innovation for instant captions. A keyboard is used to type the message which may then be either erased or memorised and recalled at random. Often facilities for rolling or crawling the messages are available. The character shapes are, however, rather plain.

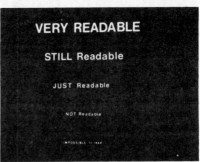

Readability

Do not use lettering that is too small to be read comfortably. Although the camera can sometimes move closer, this will usually spoil the overall proportions or lose information in other parts of the caption.

Simple animation

Here black slides of thick card cover lettering in the openings. On cue, each slide uncovers a word which appears instantly on the TV screen. The camera's shot is electronically set down to obscure the mechanics, so that only white letters are visible against a dense black background.

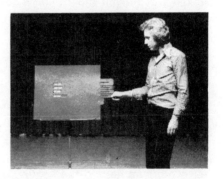

Animated motion

Here the flow of air across an aerofoil is suggested by a patterned disc moving behind a stencilled graphic.

83

Lighting: Overall System

Any TV lighting system has to provide the correct quantity of light on the subject (illumination) and, for colour television, must also provide light of the correct quality (colour temperature). To satisfy these needs it requires light fittings (luminaires), means of supporting them and a system for controlling the light output from each lamp.

How elaborate our facilities need to be, will be influenced by:
1. Type of camera being used.
2. Size of acting area.
3. Height of lighting ceiling (lighting grid).
4. Turn round time required between programmes.

Lighting equipment is expensive and, if the initial design is for a simple lighting suspension but more flexible arrangements are likely to be needed at a later date, the ceiling and steelwork to meet the later requirements should, if possible, be put in at the time of building the studio. It is difficult and expensive to add these features later.

Type of camera
The sensitivity of the camera channel determines the light intensities required. This sensitivity will be based on the camera tube (Vidicon, Plumbicon, or Image Orthicon) and the type of studio operation — monochrome or colour.

Size of acting area
In the small TV studio the whole of the available staging area is gradually used and our lighting set-up needs to accommodate several adjoining regions. The precise nature of the action in each changes for each programme and the lighting system must be flexible enough to cater for these different situations. If initially, for economy reasons, only part of the studio is being used, the lighting system can be restricted accordingly. This will cut costs but will make the system less adaptable — it will not be able to handle several set-ups simultaneously.

Height of studio grid
The height of the studio has been discussed earlier (page 18). The maximum height of the luminaires above the studio floor is directly related to this and so also is the maximum lamp throw (lamp-to-subject distance). This factor coupled with camera sensitivity fixes the wattage of the luminaire.

Turn round time
How long it takes to modify a lighting set-up to suit a new production is largely determined by the suspension system, and is discussed fully under that title later (page 86/88). Generally, the more flexible systems offer the quickest turn round.

STUDIO LIGHTING LEVELS (1 LUMEN/m² = 1 LUX)	POWER REQUIREMENTS (BASED ON THE TOTAL STUDIO FLOOR AREA)
500 – 800 LUMENS/m²	250 WATTS/m²
1000 – 1600 LUMENS/m²	500 WATTS/m²

STUDIO CAMERA TUBE	STUDIO LIGHTING LEVEL	MEAN OPERATING LENS APERTURE
MONOCHROME CAMERAS		
3″ IMAGE ORTHICON	300 – 350 LUX	f 5·6
4½″ IMAGE ORTHICON	500 – 600 LUX	f 5·6
1″ VIDICON	1200 – 1600 LUX	f2·8
1″ LEAD OXIDE VIDICON	250 LUX	f2·8
1¼″ (30mm) LEAD OXIDE VIDICON	500 LUX	f4·0
3 TUBE COLOUR CAMERAS		
3 x 1″ LEAD OXIDE VIDICONS	750 LUX	f2·8
3 x 1¼″ LEAD OXIDE VIDICONS	1000 – 1600 LUX	f4·0
3 x ⅔″ VIDICONS	2000 LUX	f2·0

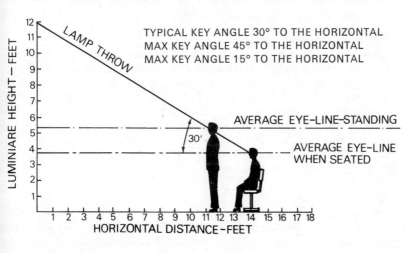

TYPICAL KEY ANGLE 30° TO THE HORIZONTAL
MAX KEY ANGLE 45° TO THE HORIZONTAL
MAX KEY ANGLE 15° TO THE HORIZONTAL

LAMP THROW

AVERAGE EYE-LINE-STANDING

AVERAGE EYE-LINE WHEN SEATED

30°

LUMINIARE HEIGHT – FEET

HORIZONTAL DISTANCE – FEET

STUDIO LIGHTING REQUIREMENTS

85

Simple Lighting Supports

The lighting suspension system provides the means for positioning the luminaires in the studio. It should:
1. Be of sufficient height to enable the correct lamp throw and vertical lighting angle to be achieved. (We must avoid steep or overhead lighting.)
2. Allow the lighting director to position his luminaires to within 0·6m (2 ft.) of any point in the studio.
3. Be easy to move luminaires around the suspension system.

Floor stands
Luminaires mounted on extendable floor stands are useful for static situations but have many disadvantages. They are generally limited in height to about two metres and can obstruct cameras, boom and artists. They are liable to be knocked, disturbing the setting of the luminaire and perhaps even causing it to fall over. Placed upstage (i.e. in distant areas of the scene) a stand-mounted luminaire has to be hidden to avoid its appearing in shot.

Despite these criticisms, however, a selection of floor stands can prove very useful for lighting through scenic openings (windows), and where we need to add an extra luminaire quickly.

Luminaires on flats
There are various fixtures available for mounting luminaires on flats. These have two main limitations. Heavy lamps cannot be used (the scenery would probably fall over!) and, obviously, lamps can be attached only where suitably constructed scenery exists.

Lightweight telescopes
This is a very flexible system but has the disadvantage that it can be used only for lightweight luminaires and where studio construction permits. It consists of concentric telescopic tubes which have large rubber pads on both ends. To use, one end of the pole, which is spring loaded, is compressed, and the pole length adjusted to the ceiling height. The spring loaded section is then released. This jams the pole firmly between the floor and the ceiling. Luminaires can be attached to the pole, or, by using an additional vertical pole, a cross member can be fitted, to enable further lamps to be included.

Lightweight track
This system is useful for studios of limited height (up to 3m). The luminaires use a special mounting which enables them to be slid along a power track fastened to the ceiling. By dividing the ceiling up with a number of separately powered tracks, good coverage of the studio can be obtained. The limitation of this system is the weight restriction on the light fittings used.

LIGHTING SUPPORTS

Lightweight stands
The lightweight stand (1) should only be used with lightweight luminaires. The "turtle" (2) is used when a luminaire is to be floor mounted. Short stands (3) (15 in) are also useful, as is a clamp arm which can be fitted to normal stands to enable a luminaire to be mounted lower than 3 ft. Wind-up stands (4) are also used for heavy luminaires.

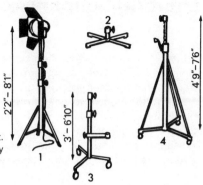

Scenic clamps
Lightweight lamps can be inserted into clamps attached to scenic flats. Here are two types, one to mount on the top of the flat (5), the other has a drop-arm to lower the height of the luminaire (6).

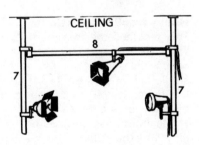

Lightweight telescopic tubes
Spring-loaded telescopic tubes (7) wedge between ceiling and floor, to support lightweight lamps. Auxiliary cross-tubes (8) can be introduced. The system provides considerable flexibility for confined spaces.

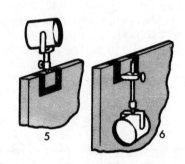

Lightweight ceiling track
Lightweight ceiling track – easy to install. Currently tracks are available which have 1, 2 and 4 separate circuits. On the multi-circuit track, connection is made to the appropriate circuit by means of sliding contacts (9).

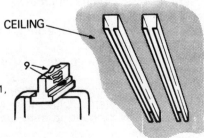

Lighting Suspension Systems

A flexible lighting suspension system is one which allows for easy and rapid positioning of a luminaire to within 0·6m of any position in the studio. This enables a short turnround time to be achieved and allows the lighting director to position his lamps in a reasonably precise way. Flexibility usually requires an expensive suspension system. The most elaborate facilities (lighting bars on motorised hoists, and motorised telescopic methods) are not included here, as their high cost is not usually justified for the small television studio.

Pipe grid

This system has the advantages of being relatively cheap, and easy to modify. All the piping and clamps are standard construction items. The grid consists of a horizontal framework made from tubular piping of 50mm diameter. The spacing between the grid members should ideally be 1·2m (4 ft.). The height of the grid should be at least 3m (10 ft.) — remember that any suspended lamp will be hanging below this. The preferred grid height is 3·6m (12 ft.). It offers a good lamp height, and it is reasonably easy to move equipment around. If the grid is above 4·2m (14 ft.) lamp-handling is more difficult.

Extra flexibility can be achieved by including a number of drop-arms or lightweight pantographs. The pantographs are more complex and expensive, but allow rapid adjustment of the luminaire height.

Heavy track suspension

This provides the maximum flexibility of the systems discussed here. The basic arrangement consists of a number of heavy duty tracks from which the luminaires on pantographs are suspended. A minimum studio height of 4·8m (16 ft.) is required. Each track is fitted with four luminaires which can be moved along it. The system is extremely flexible if the luminaires are dual source i.e. spotlight/softlight.

Maximum use is made of the luminaires if the tracks run along the *length* of the studio. The spacing of the tracks must be such that two luminaires on adjacent tracks can pass each other. A track spacing of 1·2m (4 ft.) is a good compromise. Power is extended to the luminaires by a catenary system.

The method for adding extra luminaires (e.g. for effects) depends on the type of track used.

To allow for lighting from above a cyclorama, a peripheral lighting rail is added.

If the studio ceiling is not strong enough to take the weight of such suspension systems plus the luminaires, additional supporting steelwork may be built up from the studio floor in the form of tubular pole 'ladders'.

SUSPENDED LIGHTING

Suspension methods

1. Lighting grid. Cheap, easy to install and modify if requirements change. Most suitable for low ceiling heights.
2. *Drop arm* used to lower the lamp height by a fixed amount. Its length may be pre-adjusted.
3. *Telescopic drop arm* of adjustable length allows lamp height to be altered readily over a couple of feet.
4. *Pantographs* are adjustable over a wider range.

Ceiling power tracks

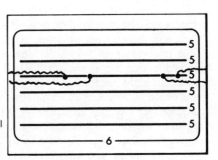

Heavy duty suspension tracks may span the ceiling (5). Here four luminaires run on each track, powered from catenary tracks. They may be supplemented by a peripheral track (6).

Types of suspension track

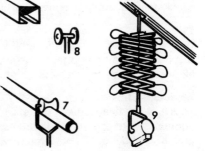

7. Scaffold pole type track. 8. Heavy duty track.
9. Example of luminaire and pantograph suspended on heavy duty track.

Lighting: Outlets & Dimmers

The simplest form of lighting system is shown opposite. This is cheap, but not very flexible. In order to change the light intensity on a particular area the luminaire has to be moved, or the spot/flood mechanism has to be operated (on soft-edged spotlights). Alternatively, part of the luminaire lens can be obscured, for example by using 'wires' (Windolite) which reduce the light by approximately 25%, or the wattage (power-rating) of the lamp can be changed. Dual-wattage lamps provide alternative outputs by filament-switching.

Routing

Extra flexibility is obtained if a dimmer is used for every lighting circuit That can be expensive, so a patching (power-routing) system is often used where a studio has a large number of outlets, not all of which are used simultaneously. In addition to the advantage of installation economy this allows for re-routing, should a dimmer develop a fault.

Number of outlets

How many outlets do we need, and where should they be situated? To decide on the number of power outlets we require, we need an estimate of the number of lamps we are likely to require in a given area.

A rough rule of thumb for the number of suspended luminaires required is 'one for every 3m² (30 sq. ft.) of studio area'. This should ensure sufficient luminaires for most programmes and avoid the need for too much movement of luminaires between programmes. The number required for say a 90m² (900 sq. ft.) studio would be 30 luminaires (say 20 hard sources and 10 soft sources).

The number of extra outlets to be included for special effects (e.g. pattern projectors) depends on the type of programmes envisaged, but generally 10 more outlets should be sufficient. If the cyclorama cloth is to be lit from above (not by a ground row), extra outlets should be included in the lighting grid.

Around the studio wall sufficient outlets should be included for lamps on the ground (e.g. ground rows for cyloramas and backdrops), for luminaires on stands, and for 'practical' lamps (i.e. table lamps, wall brackets, and similar domestic fittings in the settings).

Phase

Where possible the power supply to the studio should be one phase. But if more than one phase is used, for safety reasons it is essential that all floor outlets are on the same phase as the technical equipment.

Extensions

To allow for fixed power outlets to be extended, the studio should be equipped with a number of extension cables with single and multi-way distribution boxes. These should have robust plugs and sockets.

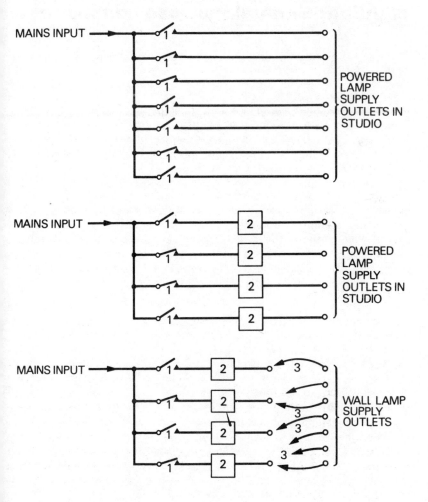

LIGHTING CONTROLS

Switched only circuits

In this simple system, switched power (1) is available at all the lamp-supply sockets (outlets).

Dimmer circuits

Here each power channel incorporates a dimmer (2), to enable the intensity of its associated lamp(s) to be adjusted. A switch is usually included in each circuit.

Patching systems

In a cheaper more flexible system, a large number of lamp supply points (3) can be connected by a patching system, to a limited number of power points. (Wall outlets into which lamps plug are not powered until patched.)

91

Lighting: General Purpose Luminaires

The general-purpose luminaires required are soft edged spotlights and soft sources.

Soft-edged spotlights

The fresnel spotlight produces a soft-edged beam of light which can be adjusted from narrow angle (spotted) to wide angle (flooded). In the fully flooded condition it behaves like a point source and produces hard edged shadows. It is a good modelling light and can be used as a keylight, backlight and for scenic lighting.

The luminaire can be fitted with *barn doors* which are used to restrict the area illuminated. The barn doors are most effective in controlling the shape of the light beam when the luminaire is fully flooded.

In colour studios twin filament lamps may be used. These give added intensity adjustment because a luminaire can now provide a wide range of illumination values at a reasonable high colour temperature. Fresnel spotlights are available in a wide range of maximum wattages — 150W (inky-dink), 500W (pup), 1kW, 2kW, 5kW and 10kW.

Soft sources

A soft source is one which produces diffuse, shadowless light. To achieve this it needs to have a large area which is obtained in several ways:

1. By using a frosted or opal bulb in an open reflector (scoop).
2. By grouping together many internal reflector (sealed beam) lamps in one housing e.g. 10-lite, mini-brute, nest.
3. By grouping four linear sources (strip lights) in a housing with suitable reflectors. This is used in colour studios and allows for dual wattage operation by switching out opposite pairs of light sources.

Soft sources are not usually fitted with barn doors, so to reduce the sideways spread of light the units are fitted with spill rings or louvred openings.

The prime use of a soft source is as a filler light but, because of its wide, even spread of illumination it is often used for lighting backcloths and cycloramas.

For ease in setting the luminaire, pole-operated controls can be fitted. These adjust the spot/flood mechanism (on spotlights), pan and tilt functions, and on dual wattage luminaires — the operating wattage. Luminaires used in colour studios should have a means of fixing colour media (colour filters) in front of it.

Tungsten halogen light sources used in many of these luminaires have the advantages (over normal tungsten sources) of longer life and a more compact envelope which does not darken during its life.

Open luminaires have the advantage that they use high efficiency lamps, are of small size and lightweight, but the disadvantage in that barn doors are not very effective in shaping the light beam.

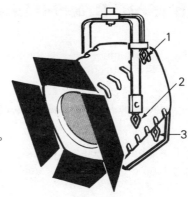

Fresnel spotlight
Soft edged spotlight, typically the beam angle can be varied from 10° (spot) to 60° (flood). Controls can be pole operated
1. Pan
2. Tilt
3. Spot/Flood

Soft sources
4. Scoop, using 500 watt or 1000 watt lamps.
5. 10 lite, using 10 × 150 W/200 W overrun reflector lamps.
6. Dual wattage soft source, using 4 × $1\frac{1}{4}$ kW (or 4 × 625 W) linear sources which can be switched off in pairs.

Open luminaires
7. 800 watt lightweight flood.
8. 1250 watt broad source.
9. Clamps to attach lightweight lamps to scenery.
Safety Note: Open luminaires should *not be used without a front protective glass or fine mesh* (2 mm) to avoid accidents if a bulb should explode.

93

Lighting: Special Luminaires

These can be categorised as luminaires used for cyclorama lighting and for special effects lighting.

Cyclorama lighting

General-purpose luminaires can be used to light a cyclorama, but the most efficient method is to use luminaires especially designed for this purpose. A ground row produces a 'natural' effect i.e. lighter at the horizon, with gradual reduction in illumination towards the top of the cyc. (A multi-unit allows for colour mixing on a white cyc.) The disadvantage of the ground row is the studio floor space it takes up, and the need to hide the lighting units behind suitable scenery (coving). Currently, there are suspended luminaires available designed to produce even illumination of the cyclorama from top to bottom. These have the advantage of leaving a clear floor — very useful in a small studio.

Special effects lighting

The hard-edged projector is used to project an image of a brightly illuminated circular aperture *or* the profile of any inserted metal stencil or mask. It can project a considerable variety of sharp or defocused images to add interest to an otherwise plain background. It can be fitted with internal metal shutters, which shape the beam with precision to light a defined area.

Hard-edged projectors are available as 500W, 1kW and 2kW units and beam angles range of 11° (narrow), 20° (normal) and 36° (wide). Equipment developments continue. Currently a 1kW projector is available which has a variable beam-angle of 22-36°. This is a very efficient luminaire and offers great flexibility, by changing the front element of its lens system, the beam angle becomes 35-45° and by changing the complete lens assembly it becomes 10-22°.

Transparency projectors are used to project still or moving effects e.g. clouds, water ripple, flames, etc. High definition lenses are required for still projection, but for moving effects satisfactory results are obtained with a simpler lens system. Projector lenses of focal length 75 100 and 150 mm (3, 4 and 6 in.) give flexibility in throw and image size.

The major problem when using these projectors for large-area effects, is in obtaining an image with sufficient brightness without melting the transparency in the process!

A relatively new light source, the compact-source iodide lamp (CSI lamp) is proving useful as a light source for projector applications, owing to its high efficiency and compactness. It is a discharge device, requiring auxiliary starting equipment, including a current limiting choke. It has a warm-up period of approximately one minute before reaching full intensity.

Cyclorama lighting

1. Ground row containing 4 × 625 watt linear lamps. For monochrome TV, units spaced 4 ft apart should be adequate.
2. Suspended luminaire for lighting a cyc uniformly from above. Available in 1 unit, 2 unit and 4 unit form. Each has 625 watt or 1.25 kW linear light sources.

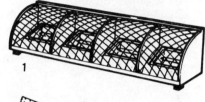

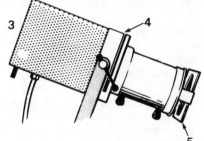

Hard-edged projector

3. 1 kW "silhouette" projector with adjustable beam angle 22°–36°
4. Slot for metal cut out.
5. Holder for colour media.

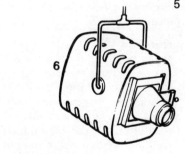

Transparency projectors

6. 2 kW projector for $3\frac{1}{4}$ in × $3\frac{1}{4}$ in still slides.
7. 2 kW projector for moving effects, e.g. clouds, fire, rain, smoke, etc., from a revolving glass disc.

Lighting Control: Dimmers

A dimmer is an electrical device used to control the light output from a luminaire. It should:
1. Provide continuously variable control of the light output.
2. Be easy to remotely control the dimmer with a simple fader.
3. Dim the light progressively, with an approximately square law, which should not vary with the load, whether it be a 2kW or 150W lamp.
4. Not be wasteful of power.
5. Not cause interference to other equipment and be silent in operation.
6. Be compact.
7. Be easy to maintain.

Dimmer types

Various types of dimmer have been used in television: resistance, saturable reactor, auto-transformer, thyratron, thyristor or silicon controlled rectifier (SCR). Unless one is purchasing secondhand equipment, the thyristor dimmer is preferable.

The complete dimmer uses two semi-conductor thyristors connected back-to-back, to make full use of the mains supply on the positive and negative half cycles. A control amplifier is necessary to convert the d.c. from the fader into a suitable gating waveform (switch-on pulse).

Interference

The thyristor dimmer satisfies most of the requirements listed above except one — interference. The very rapid switch-on of the load current can cause pulses of interference at 100 Hz (and harmonics of 100 Hz) on to adjacent microphone cables. This can also cause excessive vibrations of the lamp filament in the luminaire.

The interference can be reduced by:
1. Including an inductor in the dimmer circuit. This reduces the rate of rise of the load current and results in reduced interference and less filament vibration.
2. Using special screened quad cable for microphone circuits. This produces a marked decrease in interference pick up (28 dB) and is used in many major TV studios.

Rack mounting

Thyristor dimmers are normally rack mounted in the form of plug-in units. They should have forced ventilation to prevent them over-heating. Excessive heat causes the thyristors to function in an unpredictable manner and eventually to stop rectifying.

Some dimmer manufacturers are using a SCR type device called a triac. This is a single component which behaves like two SCRs back-to-back.

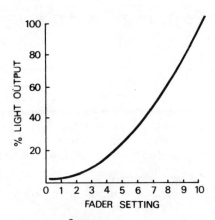

Fader setting

The fader follows an approximately square law, providing an *apparently* linear change of illumination with fader movement.

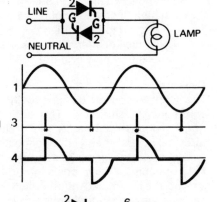

Silicon controlled rectifiers

1. Waveform of the sinusoidal mains voltage applied to the silicon controlled rectifiers (2).
3. Waveform of the gating pulses applied to switch the S.C.R. gate ("G").
4. Resultant load-current waveform.

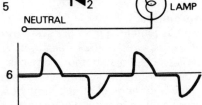

Reducing interference

5. Basic S.C.R. dimmer circuit with the inductor (6) included for interference suppression.
6. Waveform of the load current, showing the effect of the inductor on the rise time of the current.

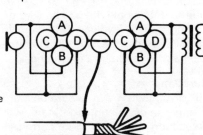

Star quad cable

Special balanced star quad cable used for microphone circuits to obviate interference pick-up. Conductors A and B form one leg and C and D form the other leg of the microphone circuit.

97

Lighting Console

The function of the lighting console is to enable the lighting director to:
1. Swiftly adjust the light output from the luminaires in use and so achieve a good *lighting balance* (i.e. appropriate relative intensities).
2. Carry out any lighting changes required by the production.
3. Reduce the heat build-up in the studio and power used, by switching out luminaires not immediately required. This also reduces the possibility of light spilling from adjacent sets.

Console design
The lighting console should be located in the vision control area. It should preferably:
1. Be compact to facilitate one-man operation.
2. Offer switching and brightness control on all the lighting channels.
3. Be designed to facilitate productional lighting changes.
4. Provide facilities for the quick selection and switching of a group of channels (memory system).

Presets
The simplest console design provides one fader to each channel, with a communal master fader. This arrangement does not offer any presetting of dimmer levels. A more elaborate system using two faders (presets) per dimmer, with two master faders is more adaptable.

While we are using one set of faders (and the appropriate master fader) to control the lamps alight in the studio, the second set of faders can be preset to suit the next lighting condition required. On cue, we can change the studio lighting to the second condition by cross-fading between the master faders. Extra grouping facilities can be obtained by using switches.

Memories
Simple switching memory systems can be used to increase the number of groups which can be selected.

These simple memory devices only store the on/off information. There are more elaborate console designs which can store the precise dimmer settings of all the lamps used in a lighting plot. However, such a console is necessarily expensive, and the production lighting requirements would have to be very demanding to justify its inclusion.

For studios involved with more complex productions a mimic-lamp panel showing the lighting channels and studio outlets in use is also desirable. It enables a quick check of the lighting plot to be made.

Load meter
Finally, a load meter should be included near the lighting console to indicate the production lighting power consumption. It should have some indication of the maximum permissible load.

Preset system

In this basic 10 channel control system there are two faders per channel and two master faders. The remote control signal to the 10 dimmers can thus be routed via a master fader and a channel fader by two routes. The dimmer always operates at the higher of the two control signals. With this system two lighting conditions can be preset and faded up or crossfaded by the appropriate master fader.

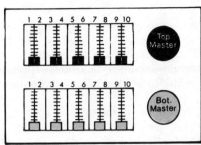

Double preset system

This 15 channel system is an extension of the above system. The two channel faders are grouped to a master fader by the three position switch i.e. UP – TOP MASTER; MIDDLE – OFF; DOWN – BOTTOM MASTER. In this way four lighting conditions can be preset and faded up using the appropriate master fader.

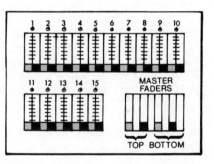

Matrix system

This 40 channel system has one, two or three faders per channel. Any of the faders can be grouped to any of the 10 master faders by means of a plug matrix panel. Thus 10 different lighting conditions can be preset which can be faded up or crossfaded by using the appropriate master fader.

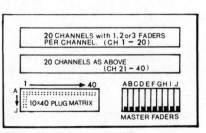

99

Microphone Assessment

Before buying microphones it is obviously necessary to take all reasonable steps to ensure that those purchased will be satisfactory. Below is a check list of questions which, while not complete, should go some way towards helping the buyer to obtain the most satisfactory microphones for his requirements.

Technical characteristics

Is the frequency response graph satisfactory and, more important, is the audio quality adequate as judged by listening tests using a high grade loudspeaker?

What is its directivity pattern (see page 102) and how constant are its directional characteristics with frequency? Is the pattern selectable, and if so how—remotely switchable or on the microphone itself? What electrical load (impedance) does the microphone require, and is this compatible with your existing equipment? How sensitive is the microphone? Does it require power supplies, and if so what types are available—mains or battery or both? If mains units are needed, are they suitably safe, and how many microphones can be powered from each unit? In the case of battery units what type of battery is needed, and how many operating hours can one set of batteries provide? Are 'battery-test' checks incorporated? Does moving the microphone around produce spurious rumbles in the output? How prone is it to wind-noise and blasting? Are windshields available and how effective are they?

Mechanical characteristics

Does the microphone appear rugged and well made? Is the cable-entry robust and likely to withstand pulling, and is the plug itself robust?

What mic-stand and sound-boom adaptors are available? What thread sizes do these have?

How big and how heavy is the mic? It its appearance likely to be satisfactory if it is seen in shot. Is the finish shiny and therefore likely to cause 'flaring' in the picture?

In the case of electrostatic microphones, are the capsules interchangeable? Are there extension tubes?

Cost and reputatuion

Are the manufacturers well known? Do they have local agents? What do you know of their spares and repair service? What guarantees do they give? How long has the microphone you are considering been in production? Is it likely to go out of production in the near future?

How much does it cost and does this include cables and power units? How expensive are the accessories?

Transducer system	— electrostatic using FET
Directivity pattern	— cardioid capsule normally supplied but but interchangeable with other capsules, e.g. omni, gun.
Power supplies	— 50V d.c. *Phantom* power. Battery unit using 9v battery, with battery life of 40 hours.
Impedance	— Nominally 200Ω balanced output. Minimum load impedance 500Ω
Sensitivity	— −39dB rel. to 1V/N/m² (−59dB rel. to 1V/dyne/cm²).
Connectors	— 3-pin DIN or XLR type, as ordered.

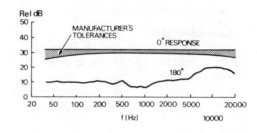

Frequency response (cardioid capsule)

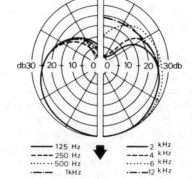

Directivity Pattern (cardioid capsule)

Accessories	— Mounting swivel bracket "Gun" tube. Pistol grip for "gun" 30 mm and 130 mm extension tubes. Foam and metal mesh windshields.
Dimensions	— 147 mm long, 18 mm diameter.
Weight	— 120 gm.
Finish	— matt.

101

Microphone Categories

The directivity pattern (or polar diagram) of a microphone indicates its response to sounds from different directions. The most important directivity patterns are omni-directional, figure-of-eight and cardioid.

Omni-directional
Sound pick-up is normally independent of angle of incidence, but in fact this is only the case at the lower frequencies (typically below 2-4 kHz).

Omni-directional microphones may be of limited use for general sound pick-up in television studios because of their inability to reject studio noise, reverberation, etc. However, they are used extensively as vocalist's hand-held microphones.

Figure-of-eight
The two 'dead' sides can be invaluable in discriminating against unwanted nearby sounds; for example in a multi-microphone balance where source-separation is important. However, microphones in this category tend to be prone to rumble when moved, and consequently can normally only be used in static situations.

Cardioid
These are widely used in television studios, because when pointed at an artist their 'dead' sides can be directed more-or-less toward areas of noise in the studio. They are widely used in booms, and here the 'dead' side is primarily of value in rejecting studio reverberation, so that for a given sound perspective (page 126) the microphone can be used farther from the performer than an omni-directional microphone could be.

Gun microphones
So called because of their shape, gun microphones have a narrow angle of pick-up at the higher frequencies, although at low frequencies they possess a cardioid or even almost omni-directional characteristic. A good gun microphone can have an impressive rejection of unwanted sounds, including reverberation, from the sides and rear. Hand-held on a pistol grip attachment, a gun microphone can often be used effectively for sound pick-up in difficult studio situations where a boom is unsatisfactory. It should be noted, however, that gun microphones rarely work well in small rooms.

Variable directivity
Inevitably these are relatively expensive. However, the cost may be justified because, by operation of a switch, either on the body of the microphone or on a remote box, the directivity pattern can be changed from omni-directional to cardioid, to figure-of-eight (but *not* gun) or indeed intermediate patterns.

102

MICROPHONE RESPONSE PATTERNS

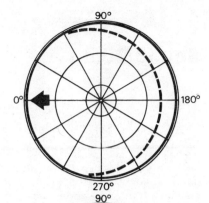

Omnidirectional
Sensitivity is more-or-less equal all round.

Cardioid
Some degree of directionality is introduced to produce a heart-shaped response curve.

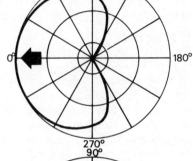

Figure-of-eight
Bi-directional sensitivity allows equal response in opposite directions.

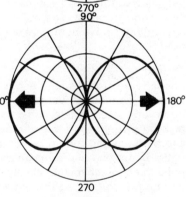

Highly directional
Special constructions, such as the gun mic, allow small sources to be pinpointed.

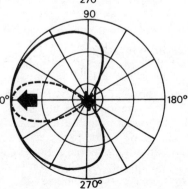

- - - - - high frequencies
———— low frequencies

Sound Boom

Of all the ways of positioning microphones in a television studio the sound-boom is easily the most versatile. It can be used to position, pan and tilt a microphone with considerable precision. Correct sound perspectives (see page 126) can usually be adjusted readily to match each shot, and where, for example, two people walk around talking, a good balance between their voices can still be obtained as the shot changes. It must be added, however, that a boom is only as good as the man operating it, and this is no easy task. A really good boom operator is not likely to have attained his skill in a matter of days or even weeks of practice.

Fishing rod
The very simplest type of boom is that often referred to as a 'fishing rod' or 'fish pole'. This consists of a suitable length of strong but light pole with the microphone attached to one end and the operator holding the other end. The pole cannot normally be more than about 2m (6ft. 6in.) in length because of the difficulty of holding it steady. This device can be very useful for coverage of sound in awkward corners of a set, but to avoid undue operator fatigue sequences of this sort should be of fairly short duration. The main drawback to the fishing rod is that the microphone movements are limited because its angle to the pole is fixed.

Studio
The full-size studio sound boom is, naturally, a very expensive item but it has a remarkable versatility in the hands of a good operator. The boom arm itself is telescopic so that the 'reach' can be varied. It can also be swung and tilted through wide angles The microphone itself can be tilted and turned by controls at the operator's position, and the entire boom and platform can be raised or lowered using a hydraulic or pneumatic mechanism. Finally, the three wheels of the trolley (or 'pram') may be set so that only the steerable wheel can turn or alternatively, all three wheels are linked to turn together, so permitting 'crabbing' along the floor.

Boom operation
A few points for the boom operator are:
1. As a very rough rule a satisfactory position for the microphone is about arm's reach away from the artist, at about 45° up in the air.
2. The position of key lights, etc. must be noted so that boom shadows in the picture can be avoided. Incidentally, the position of the boom shadow in relation to the artist's shadow can be a very useful guide.
3. Camera positions, zoom angles, etc., must be memorised at rehearsal. A camera zooming to a wide angle can leave an unwary operator with most of his boom in shot.

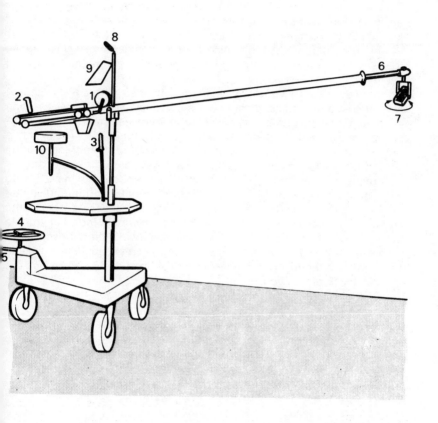

MICROPHONE BOOM

The boom arm's length (3–6 metres) is adjusted by a wheel (1), and pivoted in its central cradle. The microphone can be tilted and rotated by a control lever (2). The overall height of the boom arm and platform can be adjusted (3) between 1 and 1.5 m. The boom pram is steerable (4) and can be held stationary by a brake (5).
(6) Extending section. (7) Microphone in cradle. (8) Talk-back mic. (9) Script board. (10) Seat.

Radio Microphone

The term radio microphone is usually something of a misnomer because in most cases the microphone itself is a conventional device. It is simply fed into a miniature transmitter/receiver system.

The advantage of the radio microphone is that a performer can move freely over a relatively large area without the hindrance of trailing cables.

There are two drawbacks to radio microphones. One is their relatively high cost and the second is that they are inevitably less reliable than a conventional microphone cable. With modern electronics the reliability is normally good, but care has to be taken to avoid areas in the studio where pick-up is poor because of radio blackout or interference. In the VHF band used by most devices there is always a risk of 'multipath' interference or screening by metal structures. Consequently in setting up for a programme, it is advisable to check carefully all the anticipated positions of the microphone's transmitter, and choose carefully the siting of the receiver aerial. We should not overlook, too, that trouble can arise when a camera moves into the vicinity of either transmitter or receiver, so during rehearsal a member of the crew should be available to re-position the receiver. (Diversity reception systems can reduce the risks of 'black-out' regions.)

Battery life
A miniature transmitter must contain small-sized batteries and consequently the operating life of the batteries is fairly short, even with the modest powers radiated by most transmitters of this type. A life of 4-6 hours is typical. It is usually good practice to put new batteries in the transmitter for each programme (assuming the bare minimum of an hour or two's rehearsal followed by the transmission or recording).

Interference
It is advisable, when buying radio microphones, to check that there are no local sources of serious radio interference on the same frequency as that of the intended purchase. The limited range of the average transmitter makes it unlikely that it would interfere with other services or equipment, but the converse situation could be, at worst, disastrous.

Hiring
In the UK there are commercial organisations which hire out radio microphones on a daily basis. Bearing in mind the high cost of buying these items, hiring should be looked into if they are going to be used infrequently.

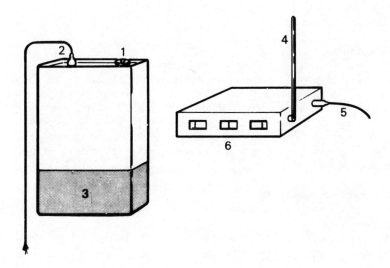

RADIO MICROPHONE TRANSMITTER
Plugging the microphone into its socket (1) switches the transmitter on. The aerial is
formed by a hanging lead (2) and by the mic. cable screening. (Batteries are located in
the base compartment (3).)

Radio microphone receiver
Carefully positioned for optimum pick-up, its aerial (4) is extended vertically. The audio
output (5) is at −70 dB. Meters (6) indicate battery level, tuning, and received signal
level.

107

Sound Mixing Desk: Design

A sound mixing desk enables the operator to perform two tasks:
1. Control the level of the programme so that reproduced sounds are neither too weak (relative to background noise), nor too loud (overloading the system and causing distortion).
2. Balance (mix) the relative outputs of sources such as microphones, tape machines, etc., to provide a combined sound signal which is artistically appropriate.

Basic design

The greatly simplified block diagram opposite illustrates a sound desk, omitting all amplifiers and refinements. Essentially each source is connected to a jack socket on the desk. The first important operational controls are the channel faders, which allow adjustment of the levels of the individual sound sources. Each channel can be switched to one of two or more *groups,* the group faders acting as sub-master controls. Finally, the groups are combined and the main (master) fader controls the level of the output signal.

Operational facilities

The more detailed operational facilities of a typical channel are set out below:
1. Preset gain — a small switched potentiometer, which allows the channel to accept a wide range of input levels (say from —80 dB to +20 dB).
2. Response selection amplifiers, and filters (page 116).
3. Echo control — determines the proportion of the channel signal to be sent to an artificial reverberation device (page 118).
4. Foldback and public address level controls (page 110).
5. Pre-hear — used to check any selected channel on a small loudspeaker to ensure that the channel and its source are functioning.
   There should also be provision (possibly by means of jacks) for the insertion of such devices as limiter/compressors (page 114).
   The above facilities, with the fader and group switching, constitute most of the requirements of a channel. The group faders may have a similar range of facilities associated with them.
   The remaining important operational features of a sound desk are:
1. Echo return fader.
2. Meter monitoring of signal level (page 112).
3. Provision for loudspeaker monitoring.
4. 'Clean feed' outputs (page 110).

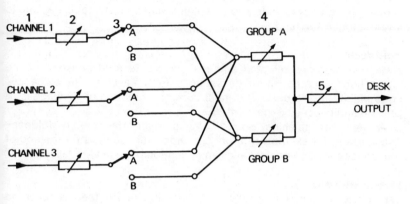

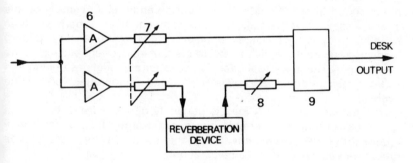

SOUND MIXING
Simplified diagram of basic sound desk
Each sound channel (1) has its associated fader (2). Channels may be linked by switching, (3) for group fading, (4) and the overall balance adjusted by the main (5) fader to keep the audio levels within the system's limits.

Simplified diagram of echo circuit
When the direct sound is mixed with its artificially reverberated version, relative proportions are controlled by an echo mixture switch (7). Buffer amplifiers (6) prevent howlround (i.e. re-amplification of an amplified output). The echo return fader (8) controls the returning reverberant sound, which is mixed in the combining circuit (9).

Sound Mixing Desk: Outputs

The main programme output of the sound desk is fed to the VT machine or the transmission network. More sophisticated designs of sound mixing desk include additional, auxiliary outputs, foldback, public address and clean feed.

Foldback

Here one or more selected sources are fed to loudspeakers on the studio floor. On most sound desks, the volume (level) of the foldback is controllable on the desk. The most common function of foldback is to provide audible cues to performers.

A feed of telecine sound played over the studio foldback loudspeaker, for example, not only provides audible cues for the end of the film sequence, but also gives an indication of pace and delivery.

Public address

Essentially similar, electrically, to foldback, the PA feed is taken to loudspeakers in the vicinity of a studio audience. It can generally be assumed that a studio audience will be unable to hear much of the direct sound from the studio floor. Consequently reinforcement of this sound is essential if the audience is to be able to hear properly and thus be able to react—i.e. laugh, applaud, etc. Directional (line-source) loudspeakers are normally needed to prevent inadvertent pick-up of the PA sound by studio microphones. These require careful positioning and suitable gain settings if 'howl-rounds' and 'colouration' are to be avoided.

The balance of the PA feed is generally different from that of the main desk output. For example, the backing group for a vocalist may require little PA reinforcement but the sound of the vocalist will probably need considerable amplification.

Clean feed

This is a feed of the main desk output *minus* one or more selected sources. Clean feeds are essential facilities if we are simultaneously using two studios with contributions from each. This arrangement ensures that the loudspeaker in each studio reproduces only the sound from the other studio. Thus howl-round or unwanted colouration can be avoided.

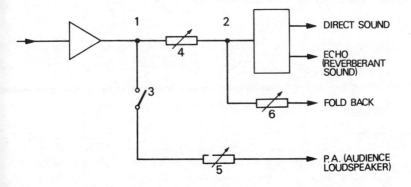

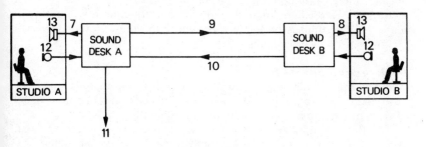

P.A. AND FOLDBACK CIRCUITS
Simplified diagram of foldback and P.A. circuits

If a P.A. or foldback system is fed from a point *before* a channel fader it will only be influenced by the system's controls, and not by fader operation. (Otherwise channel fader readjustments necessitate rebalancing the system – e.g. to prevent howlround.) The channel fader often incorporates a switch cutting the P.A. circuit when the control is faded out (backstop).

1. P.A. feed point.
2. Foldback feed point.
3. P.A. switch (often part of channel fader).
4. Channel fader.
5. P.A. volume control.
6. F/B volume control.

Clean feed and two-way working

To avoid echo or howlround effects, circuit arrangements are made for a contributor to hear a feed from the other studio, of all sounds *except* his own output. This simplified illustration outlines the method used.

7. Studio B sound only.
8. Studio A sound only.
9. Clean feed of Studio A sound.
10. Clean feed of Studio B sound.
11. Studio A+Studio B sound.
12. Microphones.
13. Speakers.

Monitoring Sound Levels

Sound signals from a mixing desk need to be monitored in two ways:
1. Using a high-grade loudspeaker for assessment of quality, balance, etc.
2. Using a suitable electrical indicator to check that the sound signal is within the prescribed limits of the system.

VU meter
The commonest indicator, is the VU (volume unit) meter, which is a voltmeter of suitable ballistic and impedance characteristics, connected across the circuit to be monitored. Although cheap, the VU meter has the drawback that it cannot register short-duration signal peaks with any accuracy, although these peaks can cause undesirable overload distortion in amplifiers, recording equipment, transmitters, etc. Such a meter is nevertheless perfectly satisfactory for line-up purposes when steady tones only are involved.

Peak programme meter
A much more satisfactory device for visual monitoring is the BBC designed Peak Programme Meter (PPM). This is a rather complex piece of equipment, and is therefore more expensive than the VU meter.

The PPM comprises, in essence, two parts: a peak-detector circuit with logarithmic amplifier, and a high grade moving coil meter. LED devices having PPM or VU "laws" are available as alternatives to conventional meters. The circuitry ensures that very short duration peaks cause a closely corresponding deflection of the meter (the pointer reaches its peak value in a few milliseconds). The logarithmic amplifier makes the meter calibration approximately proportional to the peak signal-level in decibels.

Although the meter has a very fast rise-time it has a slow recovery or fall-time—taking a few seconds to decay from full deflection to zero. This makes it much easier to read peak values and reduces eye-strain. Eye-strain is minimised by having a white pointer and a minimum number of scale divisions (in white), on a black background.

Although a very stable device, the characteristics of a PPM should be checked periodically.

It must be noted that neither the PPM nor the VU meter can be used to give an indication of sound balance. For example, although two voices may sound equally loud, meter readings can be significantly different.

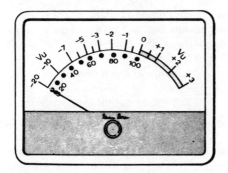

SOUND METERS
Peak programme meter
A special type of voltmeter, with a simplified logarithmic scale (in 4 dB steps). It has a rapid rise characteristic and a slower die-away time. "4" on the scale represents zero level (40% modulation). "6" represents 100% modulation.

Volume units (VU) meter
The dual scale on the VU meter includes decibels indications, and a percentage modulation scale.

Ensuring that peaks do not exceed system limits.

Automatic Level Control

The volume (level) of reproduced sounds must not be allowed to fall below or exceed the audio system's limits (page 158). This is achieved by continually adjusting the system's gain (amplification). There is no real substitute for a trained human operator in carrying out this task during a programme. No electronic device can, for example, follow a musical score and perform the anticipatory changes necessary to maintain the audio signals within prescribed limits, while still leaving the listener unaware of any restriction of the dynamic range. There are, however, occasions when a sound mixer cannot perform this controlling function entirely satisfactory (e.g. unexpected loud noises), and it is then that electronic devices called limiter/compressors are invaluable.

Limiter/compressor

Basically a limiter/compressor is a variable gain amplifier, its amplification being controlled by the level of the input or output signal.

The characteristics of a typical limiter/compressor are shown opposite. Above the threshold point, which is adjustable and shown in the diagram set at −4 dB relative to 1 mW, the gain reduction occurs by an amount which depends on the compression ratio selected. For example, using a setting of 2 : 1 the ratio

$$\frac{\text{change of input level in dB}}{\text{change of output level in dB}} = 2$$

The limiting condition represents a compression ratio of 20 : 1 or more.

An important additional control on limiter/compressors is the recovery time switch. This adjusts the time for the gain of the device to return to normal after a programme peak has caused compression or limiting. With short recovery times an audible 'noise pumping' effect may be objectionable on speech—that is the rapid fluctuations in gain can cause back-ground noise to 'pump' up and down during pauses between words. Instead, a longer recovery time may be found necessary. For other types of material, short recovery times may be appropriate.

Typical applications

Typical uses of compressor/limiters are:

1. In the desk output as a protection against overloads (excessive volume, causing distortion).

2. In microphone channels to hold constant the output of a vocalist's hand microphone. (Movements of the microphone nearer or further from the mouth naturally cause level changes which cannot be anticipated by the sound mixer.)

3. To control sudden high-volume sound effects (for example a pistol shot).

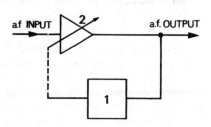

Simplified limiter/compressor
A side-chain circuit (1) samples the main programme signal, and modifies the performance of the main variable-gain amplifier (2) according to the control settings (compression ratio and recovery time).

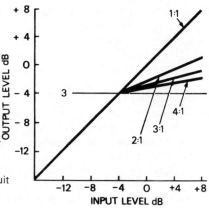

Basic parameters of a typical limiter/compressor
The limiter accommodates input levels over a range of −12 to +8 dB.
Any signal exceeding a determined level (3) causes feedback that reduces the circuit gain, bringing it within the required limits.

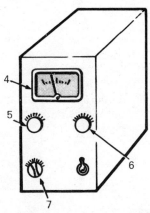

A typical limiter/compressor
The attenuation meter, calibrated in a 24 dB scale, shows the instantaneous gain reduction (4).
The threshold control (5) determines the onset point at which limiting commences.
Compression ratio/limiting selector (6) switch, determines the degree of compression.
Recovery time selector (7) for 0.1-3.2 secs.

115

Frequency Correction

There are a number of occasions where we want to alter the frequency response of a channel in a sound desk for technical or artistic reasons:
1. To match the response of one type of microphone with another, so that when cross-fading there is no obvious difference in quality.
2. To match the quality of sound on a film insert to studio sound.
3. To simulate effects such as telephone speech.
4. To improve clarity by, for example, putting in bass-cut to reduce the effects of low frequency reverberation.
5. To compensate for the fact that a microphone has to be in a position where it cannot pick up optimum sound quality.

Types of correction

Frequency correction devices can be grouped into five categories, although in some cases this grouping may be misleading because there are no sharp divisions.
1. Response selection amplifiers (RSAs)—sometimes termed equalisers — provide controllable amounts of bass cut and lift, and treble cut and lift. The subjective effects of such controls can be quite marked, but may not be sufficient to give the more extreme correction required to simulate telephone quality speech.
2. Presence circuits (often incorporated in RSAs) give a relatively narrow-band boost at selectable frequencies. Presence-cut is a corresponding reduction.
3. Octave filters (graphic equalisers) can be regarded as flexible RSAs. They usually cover 8 to 10 octaves with a sliding control giving ± 15 dB or so alteration to the level of each octave.
4. Effects units can be thought of as RSAs with a more drastic action. They can be very useful for simulating telephone speech, etc.
5. Filters, typically provide steep bass cut to reduce, for example, turntable rumble, microphone rumble, etc.
6. Parametric equalisers provide a wide range of frequency correction characteristics.

Care in use

While frequency correction devices are invaluable adjuncts to sound mixing equipment, and are commonly incorporated in the channels of many sound desks, they must always be used with discretion. Inexperienced operators should avoid using them unnecessarily. It is better to try to get the sound right in the first place than to hope to improve it by frequency correction.

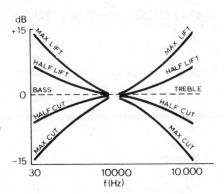

Typical equaliser (R.S.A.) curves

Although one normally aims for a flat frequency response overall, deliberate reduction or reinforcement of parts of the audio spectrum can improve reproduced sound quality.

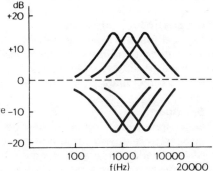

Presence filters

By boosting part of the audio spectrum, we can often enhance the illusion of subject clarity and separation. The illustration shows typical equaliser settings.

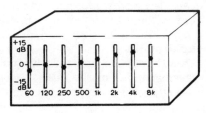

Graphic equaliser

Here slide faders adjust the system's audio response curve (e.g. at octave intervals), to modify the resultant sound quality. This design permits +15 dB to −15 dB insertion at 60, 120, 250, 500 Hz, 1 kHz, 2, 4, 8 kHz.

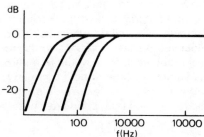

High pass filters

These filter circuits introduce a fall-off in bass to reduce distracting rumble, hum, or low-pitched vibration pick-up.

Artificial Reverberation

Apart from talks and discussions, most types of TV programme have some artificial reverberation added to improve the sound. Although not strictly accurate, the term 'echo' is widely used to describe the simulated reverberation. It can be produced by several standard devices.

Echo room

To avoid a 'boxy' sound quality, the empty room should have a volume of not less than about 50 cubic metres. The echo room is simple to equip, but the reverberation time cannot easily be altered (it should not be less than about 3 seconds), and it takes up very costly space.

Magnetic loop or drum

This can be relatively inexpensive, and quite compact. Some variation in reverberation time is usually possible but the simulated echo is liable to have a 'fluttery' nature. As a means of producing effects for pop music, such magnetic devices can, however, be quite satisfactory.

Springs

Echo springs can range from small, easily portable and inexpensive devices to relatively large and costly pieces of equipment. The former have a fixed reverberation time of about 3 seconds and tend, if used injudiciously to have a rather 'jangly' sound. On the other hand, if only a small amount of echo is used they can be quite adequate. The larger spring devices can produce a very good quality echo and they have a variable reverberation time in the range of 1.5-2 seconds minimum up to 5 seconds maximum, but are expensive.

Echo plates

These have been, until the advent of the high quality spring, the standard reverberation unit in many television organisations. Until relatively recently echo plates have been rather large and heavy, but new ones are more compact.

Plates have a variable reverberation time ranging from 1 second to about 5 seconds and the adjustment can be made remotely.

In deciding what type of echo system to buy, one should weigh carefully the cost (which is quite considerable in the high quality devices) against present and anticipated requirements. If there is seldom a need for more than minimum echo, one of the cheaper spring units may suffice. Should there be a need for extensive use of echo—in drama situations for example, and orchestral music, the high cost of plates or the larger spring devices may have to be faced.

ECHOES

Echo room
In a reverberant room, sound reproduced by a loudspeaker (1) reflects from hard surfaces, the multiple sounds being picked up by a microphone (2).

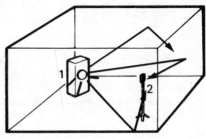

Magnetic echo device
The tape driven by a capstan and pinch wheel (3), or a coated wheel is demagnetised by the erase head (4), and the sound to be treated is recorded (5). This recorded sound is successively reproduced by replay heads (6).

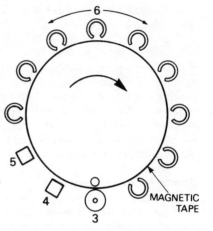

Echo spring
The sound to be treated is fed into a transducer (7) that vibrates the spring correspondingly. The mechanical vibrations resonate within the spring, and are picked up by a second transducer (8).

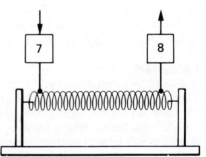

Echo plate
The drive unit (9) induces sounds in the metal sheet suspended by tensioning springs. The contact microphone (10), often a crystal mic., picks up these vibrations.

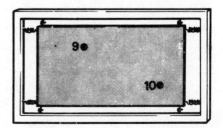

Loudspeakers

Broadly speaking, loudspeakers are used in television studios for several different purposes, such as monitoring, studio foldback, audience (PA), and intercommunication.

Monitoring

A high quality monitoring loudspeaker in the sound mixing area is essential. Such a loudspeaker must, have a wide, flat frequency range, and a good transient response (e.g. no hangover after sharp short sounds).

The only way to assess the quality of reproduction of a loudspeaker is by careful listening tests using a wide range of programme material. If possible the loudspeaker under examination should be tested in the position in which it is to be used. Its loudness range must be at least adequate for all envisaged conditions. Its directional properties should be known. Very high quality reproduction along only a very narrow beam may be less desirable than a slightly less good reproduction over a wide angle. Size and weight of the loudspeaker and its enclosure are obvious points of interest.

Studio loudspeakers

Studio-floor loudspeakers are employed both for general studio talkback and for foldback (page 110). Good quality loudspeakers should be used, although parameters are not so stringent as for monitoring purposes. Factors that are important here are portability (the loudspeaker should be mounted on a small trolley—with quiet castors!) and ruggedness. The ability to handle fairly large sound levels is desirable, although this may be required only very occasionally.

PA systems

Audience (PA) loudspeakers usually need to be directional to avoid their output being picked up by studio microphones. This directional radiation is provided in the 'line-source' ('column') type of loudspeaker. Line source loudspeakers provide intelligible sound, but of an overall quality that is inferior to that expected from the best monitoring types.

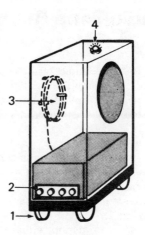

Studio loudspeakers
A mobile high-quality loudspeaker with a
wheeled base (1) and enclosed amplifier
(2), has many applications, e.g. fold back.
The audio and mains supply cables are
stored on hooks at the rear (3). An indicator
light (4) shows when the unit is powered.

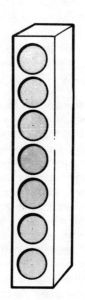

Line source loudspeaker
A columnar loudspeaker enclosure, this
provides a directional source, enabling
sound to be reproduced over a narrow
vertical angle, without danger of pick-up by
nearby audience mics.
The directivity pattern of the enclosure is
pronounced for frequencies of wavelength
less than the length of the column.

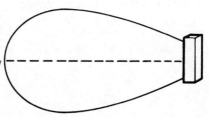

121

Audio Tape Recorders

One or more audio tape recorders are essential in the sound control area of any television studio. Typical usage includes introductory, play-out, and background music, spot sound effects, and 'off-stage' dialogue (e.g. the cries of street traders).

Types of recorder

Tape machines vary considerably in their price, quality and range of facilities. A small cassette machine costs a fraction of the price of a high quality professional reel-to-reel machine. Cassette machines are cheap, small, and easily handled, and cassettes are rapidly inserted and removed. On the other hand, their quality and background noise (signal-to-noise ratio) cannot equate with the heavier duty reel-to-reel type of machine, although more expensive cassette recorders may be sufficient for some purposes.

Unlike simpler tape-recorder designs, a reel-to-reel machine with separate record and replay heads provides an immediate continual check of recording quality, because the output of the replay head can be fed to the monitoring loudspeaker. (All recordings should, if possible, be made using this facility.)

Desirable operational features

Operational experience has shown various features to be desirable in television studio tape machines including:

1. Large (NAB type) spools giving, with standard tape, just over one hour's playing time at 19 cm/s. Removal of the centres to permit the playing of 'cine' spools should be quick and easy.

2. Frequency response, wow and flutter characteristics should be well within specifications, and regular routine checks made. Machines get heavy use, and performance can deteriorate.

3. The start/run-up time should be 'instantaneous', if accurately timed effects are to be introduced on cue.

4. Adjustments to record and replay gain, bias level, etc. should be easily accessible so that the machine is quickly lined up.

5. There should be headphone monitoring positions for both the incoming (record) signal and replayed signal. Provision must exist to permit the operator to listen to the output of the replay head when the machine output is faded down. This enables him to set the machine up to replay a particular item or effect without any risk of the spooling noise, etc. being overheard on the programme sound.

6. It should be easy to edit tape on the machine.

SPECIFICATION OF A HIGH QUALITY TAPE MACHINE

Tape speeds	38 and 19 cm/s $\pm$0·2%
	(15 and $7\frac{1}{2}''$/sec)
Tape slip	<0·1%
Wow and flutter	<0·05% at 38 cm/s
	<0·08% at 19 cm/s
Start time to reach	0·2% flutter <0·5s
Rewind time	120s for 2400 ft. reel
Max. input level	+22dB
Min. input level	0dB
Max. undistorted output level	+24dB

Frequency response

at 38 cm/s	30 Hz	—	18	kHz	$\pm$	2dB
(15"/sec)	60 Hz	—	15	kHz	$\pm$	1dB
at 19 cm/s	30 Hz	—	15	kHz	$\pm$	2dB
($7\frac{1}{2}''$/sec)	60 Hz	—	12	kHz	$\pm$	1dB

Overall signal-to-noise ratio

(at 38 cms (full track) with   61dB
CCIR equalisation)

Erase efficiency	75dB or better at 1 kHz
Bias and erase frequency	150 kHz

Disc Reproducing Equipment

While the audio tape recorder is an essential facility in TV studio operations, disc reproducers (grams) have an important role to play. Music and sound effects are invariably more readily available in disc form.

Desirable features
The following features are desirable in disc reproducers:
1. A high quality (transcription type) turntable and motor assembly (speed stability, inaudible rumble).
2. A well-designed arm is needed to ensure good tracking, minimum disc wear, etc. However, it may be necessary to choose a cartridge and stylus assembly for its robustness, even if this provides a slightly lower quality of reproduction.

Cueing
Many systems exist for providing an instant wow-free start at a selected point in a disc. In one of the more complicated designs, the disc with the pick-up lowered on it, lies on a platter resting on three supports. Operation of a switch brings the spinning turntable up to the platter, lifting it clear of its supports. The disc is thus brought up to its correct speed in little more than half a second. A muting system may 'kill' the output until this run-up time has elapsed so that an audible 'wowed start' is impossible. While quite good results can be achieved with simpler arrangements, pick-up lowering devices in general cannot give accurate cueing The slightest eccentricity on the disc means that the stylus may land in the wrong groove. Provided, though, that the run-up time is reasonably short and there are pre-fade-listen facilities (see below) good cueing can be achieved without any special devices.

By arranging an auxiliary audio output from the pick-up prior to any channel fader, we can arrange to listen to the reproduced disc without its being heard in the studio output. This pre-fade-listen (PFL) enables us to select the cueing point—to 'cue-up' the disc.

Sometimes 'slip mats' can help in cueing. These are usually discs of felt slightly larger than the turntable placed between disc and turntable. If the surface of the turntable is sufficiently slippery it can rotate freely while the slip mat is held in the fingers, the cued-up disc thus being stationary. At the right instant the slip mat is released and the channel faded up.

Although these cueing methods require operational experience, and a 'feel' of the run-up peculiarities of each machine, with care good results can be achieved.

CUEING A DISC

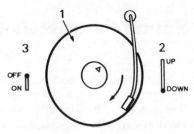

Run the disc (1) until the required point is heard on pre-fader monitoring (pre-fade listen) headphones. (Fader (2) down), and switch off turntable motor (3).

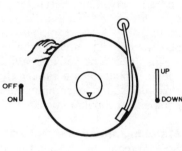

Stop the disc and turntable carefully to avoid stylus jumping grooves.

Turn disc back gently until the start of the required passage is heard. Then note position of label (4).

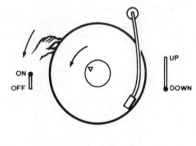

Continue turning back, noting the number of revolutions of the label until sufficient run up time has been allowed for (e.g. a two second run up time corresponds roughly to one revolution at $33\frac{1}{3}$ r.p.m.).

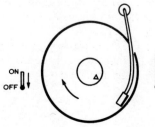

Switch on the motor the appropriate time before the sound is needed. As its label approaches the position noted in stage (iii), having made the correct number of revolutions, *fade up*. (A slip mat can often shorten the run-up time.)

Sound Perspective

Television studio sound quality may be degraded for several reasons. Acoustics are often modified unpredictably by staging (scenic) arrangements. Background noise (e.g. ventilation, equipment movement) is generally audible. Microphones often cannot be placed in their optimum positions, particularly when there is the added complication of performer movement. To some extent, although pictures can cause us to overlook slight impairment of sound quality, there should be no obvious conflict between the picture and its accompanying sound. If, for instance, a person appears to be a considerable distance away, the sound should have a similar character. Close-up pictures should have close-up sound accompaniment. The *sound perspective* and visual perspective should match.

Matching sound and picture
Sound perspective relates the apparent distance of the sound source to its picture. Our ears assess distance by evaluating relative volumes, and by noting the quality changes that arise as the ratio of direct to reflected (indirect) sound changes.

If little reflected sound is heard and the volume is relatively loud, the source will seem close. If indirect sound predominates (even if this is produced by artificial reverberation—page 118) and the source fainter, we shall interpret it as being further away.

If appropriate sound perspective is not at least partially achieved, then an inconsistency is presented to the viewer, and there is a real risk that the overall 'believability' of the programme may be reduced. We should always aim, therefore, to relate sound perspective to its picture, and to avoid at all costs such extreme incongruities as close shots of a speaker with 'distant' sound, or distant shots with close-sound perspective.

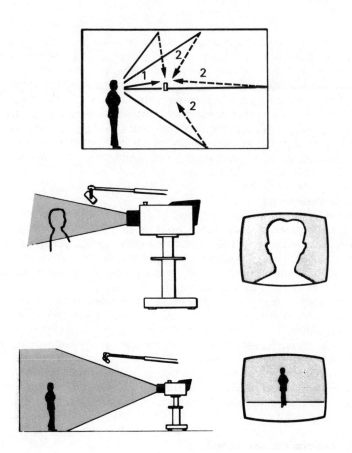

SOUND QUALITY
Direct and indirect sound
The microphone picks up a mixture of direct sound from the source (1), and reflected sounds from its surroundings (2) – walls, floor, ceiling. The closer the microphone to the source, the greater the proportion of direct sound pick-up.

Close ups
A close mic. position is required to give a sound perspective suitable for close shots.

Distant shots
For more distant shots, the microphone is positioned correspondingly farther away to provide an appropriate mixture of direct and reflected sounds.

127

Sound and Audience Participation

Programmes in which a studio audience actively participates (asking questions, contributing to discussions) present several sound coverage difficulties. A chairman, and any panel of speakers can be covered by conventional methods such as microphones on table stands. It is the contributing audience that causes problems.

Broadly there are two versions of this kind of programme—that in which the members of the audience who are going to speak are selected in advance, together with the order in which they will speak and the 'free-for-all' type of programme where the audience is largely spontaneous in its contributions.

Selected speakers

When the audience speakers are known in advance, one possible method is to have each person come up to a stand microphone, not forgetting however that there must be microphones over the audience to pick up applause, laughter and similar reactions. With the stand microphone method good quality pick-up can obviously be obtained but there is likely to be a slight interruption while a speaker leaves the seat to approach the microphone and the speaker is subjected to something of an ordeal. Consequently the 'naturalness' of the presentation may suffer.

If the audience speakers remain seated, an operator can hold a hand microphone in front of each speaker, particularly if the speakers are placed in easily accessible seats. (Note that if a radio microphone is used (page 106) it obviates the risk of awkward entanglements of cables with chairs and people.) Alternatively, a 'fishing rod' (see page 104) can be used.

Spontaneous contributions

Where audience contributions are spontaneous, the problems are greater. With a small suitably placed studio audience slung microphones can be effective in picking up comments. As a rough guide in a non-reverberant studio one cardioid microphone can cover 12 to 15 people occupying a floor area of about 6 m². Thus an audience of 60 people could be covered by five or six microphones, provided the audience is reasonably concentrated. With this number of microphones it becomes necessary to have an auxiliary sound mixer on the studio floor. He can follow the action, and fade up only the one microphone needed for each speaker, the others remaining slightly, faded down, so that comments from elsewhere will not be totally lost.

'Gun' microphones (see page 102) can be used with good effect in this type of programme because an operator can point the 'gun' at each speaker.

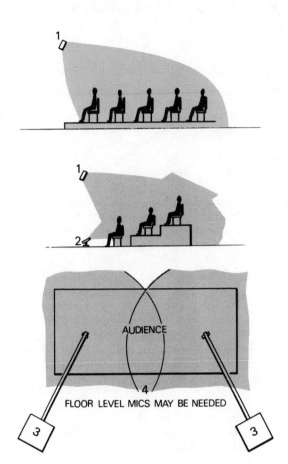

FLOOR LEVEL MICS MAY BE NEEDED

AUDIENCE SOUND

Floor audience

Where general sound is required from an audience seated at floor level, slung microphones (1) may suffice (one mic. to about 15 people).

Tiered audience

Where an audience is seated at several levels (e.g. on rostra) slung microphones (1) may need to be supplemented by a floor mic. (2) on a low stand.

Specific pick-up

Where specific individuals speak within an audience, two booms (3) may cover them as shown here. Where the chairman indicates the next speaker the most suitable boom has time to position itself. Spontaneous shots can result in delayed sound pick-up.

The borderline between the effective and the intrusive is narrow indeed.

Music and Sound Effects

A small television studio seldom has the resources that allow the luxury of specially written and performed music for incidental purposes (e.g. accompaniment to captions, etc.). Instead, commercially available recordings have to be relied upon. However, the range of these is so great that appropriate music can generally be found. (Copyright regulations must be scrupulously observed, of course.)

Use of music
In educational television productions the question sometimes arises as to whether any sort of theme music is appropriate or not. The decision must rest with the director, but if music is needed (e.g. accompany captions) the following points may be worth noting:
1. The music should be apt. It would be quite ludicrous to have the Grand March from *Aida* preceding a programme demonstrating biological dissections. A Bach Partita might be more suitable.
2. Possible unintentional puns and ironies should be looked for. Presenters with the surnames 'Hall' or 'King' probably ought not to be introduced with Grieg's *Hall of the Mountain King* (Peer Gynt) because some wag in the viewing audience is bound to cause more or less humorous distractions.
3. Current pop music should be avoided if a videotaped programme is likely to be shown at intervals over a period of years, as this will date the production quickly.
4. Music that has been used in a radio or a television series on another network certainly should not be used. Even if the series finished a few years previously there is a danger that some of the viewing audience will be trying to remember what the series was instead of concentrating on the programme in front of them.

Sound effects
These can be obtained either by using commercial discs of sound effects, or by making special recordings of the actual sound needed or a simulation of the actual sound.

Care should be taken that the sound to be dubbed is as authentic as possible. Viewers are all too ready to point out that they heard herring gulls but saw only kittiwakes! On the other hand, background effects may sometimes be played at such a low level that precise identification of the sound is difficult, so there can be some latitude in practice.

It is surprising what sounds can be produced by fairly simple manipulation of other noises. For example a door slam replayed at half speed, with possibly some frequency correction and echo, can become a convincing simulation of one heavy wooden spar striking another.

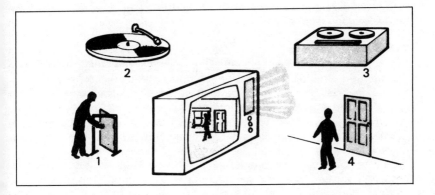

ADDITIONAL SOUNDS

Use music wisely

Music at inappropriate times only distracts from the subject in hand! Where the music is extensive and melodious, it may even preoccupy the viewer, to the exclusion of the picture.

Sound effects origins

Although a sound effect may appear to occur naturally to the audience, it may actually be produced by (1) a substitute door, (2) a library effects disc, (3) a specially recorded effect, (4) a real door in the studio.

131

Talkback in the Studio

Television relies for its success, on the efforts of a co-ordinated team. Some of the team are on the studio floor, and require continual guidance and instruction (e.g. cameras), others are located within the studio complex. To provide communication within the team, an efficient talkback system is essential. This takes several forms: general, private-wire, switched, and reverse talkback.

Production talkback
A microphone on the desk in front of the director relays his voice to cameramen (through the camera cable), boom operators, and to other floor staff who wear headphones plugged into wall sockets distributed around the studio. The floor manager has to be extremely mobile, so rather than be hampered by a long cable, he often wears an earpiece connected to his small pocket receiver. This is tuned to the studio's radio talkback transmitter. Adjoining technical areas (videotape, telecine) are equipped with talkback loudspeakers. Where talkback is to be heard outside the studio complex (e.g. in the control room at an outside broadcast point—a remote), a sound-line (control-line) is used to feed a loudspeaker or headset there.

Talkback variations
Key-operated microphones enable the technical director, sound mixer and lighting director to talk on production talkback when necessary. A further key enables technical and production control room staff to speak on the studio foldback loudspeaker, should this be necessary. When loudspeaker talkback is used, the control room loudspeaker and normal foldback sound are cut to prevent howl-round. The facility is made inoperative in transmission conditions, to prevent accidents.

For certain types of production (e.g. news, sports, actuality) the presenter wears a deaf-aid earpiece fed with switched talkback which can be operated by a push-button switch in front of the director. This facility enables the director to pass instructions, to the presenter, even when the programme is 'on the air'.

Private wire intercom
In addition to production or general talkback, various private-wire systems provide inter-specialist communication. The sound mixer requires independent sound talkback to his studio assistants; and the boom operators need to be able to converse with the sound mixer (boom reverse talkback). Similarly, the lighting director requires an independent talkback system to communicate with electricians. Also, various specialist control points (e.g. the sound mixer, vision control/lighting) have mic/loudspeaker inter-communication panels, and talkback to the director.

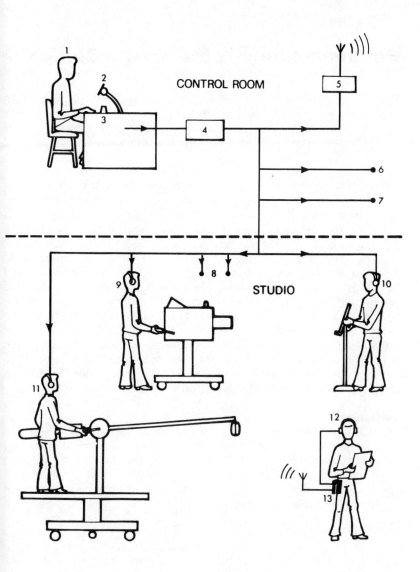

BASIC STUDIO TALKBACK SYSTEMS

A simplified illustration of the distribution of production talkback is shown. In addition private wire switched intercomm circuits exist between members of the team.

1. Director. 2. Director's microphone. 3. Microphone On/Off switch. 4. Amplifiers. 5. Talkback transmitter and aerial for radio talkback to Floor Manager. 6. Talkback distribution to other destinations in the studio complex e.g. Make-up Service Room and Video Tape and Telecine Areas. 7. Talkback distribution to destinations outside the studio complex e.g. Outside Broadcasts. 8. Distribution to studio personnel requiring talkback other than those illustrated e.g. Back Projectionists, Prompter Operator and Camera Mobile Crane Operators. 9. Cameraman. 10. Caption Operator. 11. Boom Operator. 12 Floor Manager. 13. Floor Manager's receiver and aerial.

Communication in the Studio Complex

The principal means of communication within the studio is by production talkback (page 132). This, as we have seen, is also made available to recording channels and programme contributors (e.g. telecines or outside broadcasts) outside the immediate studio area.

Signalling
Comprehensive though the talkback system may be, it can become, if used to excess a distracting background babel that either creates confusion and slows down the pace of rehearsals or is disregarded as 'intended for the other guy'. Directors can help matters by phrasing most questions so that they require only a straightforward 'yes' or 'no' answer. The cameraman can reply by rapidly tilting his camera up or down to answer 'yes' or panning right to left to answer 'no'. Rapid zooming in and out, or waving the camera around, shows that the cameraman is trying to draw the director's attention to his problem shot. Where there is a need to speak to the director he will often do so over a nearby sound-boom, or his reverse talkback circuit to the production control room desk. By the same token, telecine and videotape operators do not usually need to talk to the director. They have a button which operates a buzzer in the control room. One buzz in reply means 'yes' and two buzzes mean 'no'.

Switchboard
In addition, larger studios may be equipped with a small telephone switchboard operated by the technical director (technical manager) who can route control lines from outside destinations to different positions in the production area. Thus, where a further explanation is required (e.g. a film breakage or a machine fault) use can be made of the control line telephone link.

Lighting intercom
While in the studio adjusting lamps, the lighting director needs to retain communication with the rest of his team (assistants, vision staff, electricians). Telephones around the studio walls provide private wires to key points (lighting console, patchboard, etc.), but unquestionably the most effective method is a small two-way radio transceiver. This can considerably reduce the time taken for rigging and setting equipment.

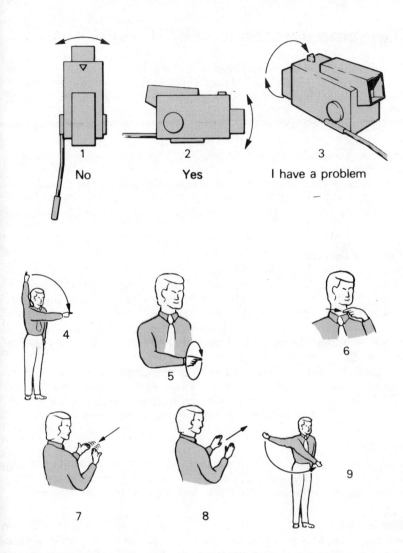

1 No   2 Yes   3 I have a problem

SIGNALS

The cameraman's signals

The cameraman can reply to talkback questions and convey simple messages by camera movement. He can shake the camera head for "NO", nod it for "YES" (2). A circular movement (or zoom jerks) means "I HAVE A PROBLEM" (3). Rapid in/out focusing shows that he cannot focus sharply on his subject(s) due to limited depth of field.

Floor manager's signals

Signals from the floor manager can provide a range of silent cues and instructions to guide performers and audience. Typical gestures include:
Cue (4),Wind up within previously agreed time (5), Cut finish immediately (6), Move downstage (7), Move upstage (8), You are off camera. Go to next position (9).

135

Film provides an important adjunct for studio production.

Telecine

Telecine machines are special types of film projector, enabling the film image to be converted directly into a video signal—without the use of an intermediary screen. Two basic designs are widely used: flying spot and vidicon types. Flying-spot designs employ a cathode ray tube (display tube) on which a scanning beam builds up a plain bright television raster. The film runs between this display tube and a photo-electric cell. The light collected by the photo-cell light continually fluctuates, corresponding with the film density at each point. A special lens or prism system compensates for film movement. Vidicon telecines are, in principle, film projectors fitted with a suitable lens system which focuses the image of the film straight on to the target of a Vidicon television camera.

Telecine control

While the film is running, the telecine operator compensates for undesirable variations in density and contrast, using his lift (black level) and gain (signal amplitude) controls in order to produce optimum picture quality. He also controls where necessary, the sound level from the optical (comopt) or magnetic (commag) sound track recorded on a stripe alongside the picture, or the synchronised track on a separate magnetically-coated film (sepmag).

Colour films may be replayed on suitably designed machines of both flying-spot and Vidicon designs. Variations in the film's colour-fidelity, and the need to match the film with the studio pictures, require the adjustment of colour correction control circuits, while the film is running.

Film gauge

Undoubtedly, the most widely used film-gauge in television is 16mm. The costs for stock and processing are much higher for 35mm. film, while conversely the quality of 8mm. film is generally unsatisfactory.

Film leader

All film picture sequences are usually preceded by a leader, which serves the dual purpose of protecting the film, and providing an exact run-up time to the first frame of picture. The leader is a standardised length of film, printed with numbered countdown frames from twelve to three, indicating the film footage from the first picture frame. (The numbers 'two' and 'one' are omitted, in case the film source is selected early by the vision mixer.) In practice the director usually cues the operator to 'run telecine' from the figure ten which allows eight seconds to reach full speed and the first frame of film. The exact cue-point can be established during rehearsals.

Where necessary, all the main operational functions can be remotely controlled.

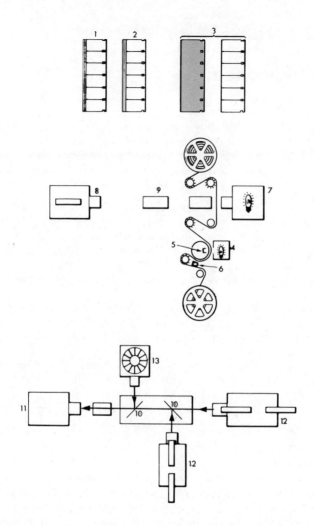

FILM

Film types

The sound recording associated with the picture may be printed as an optical image alongside the shots, (1) recorded magnetically on a stripe along the film edge (2), or recorded on a separate magnetic film run synchronously with the mute picture print (3).

Basic vidicon telecine

To reproduce an optical sound track, a light beam from an exciter lamp (4) is projected through a fine light slit onto the track, which fluctuates in density or area. A photocell (5) converts the varying light into audio signals. A magnetic sound-head (6) reproduces any commag. track. On 16 mm. film, the sound is 26 frames ahead for comopt, and 28 frames ahead for commag. tracks. (35 mm. comopt is 20 frames ahead.). The picture is illuminated by a projector (7) and viewed by a camera (8) through a lens (9).

Basic multiplex system

Optical multiplexing using semi-mirrors, (10) or prisms, enable one vidicon camera (11) to pick up the outputs of two film projectors (12) and a slide projector (13).

Film Processing

Colour and black-and-white films are available both as reversal and negative stock. Where the quality of the final result (the show-print) is the first consideration, negative stock is invariably chosen. This has several advantages, in processing correction and editing techniques.

Editing processes
When negative film is processed, an uncorrected print is made from the negatives to enable the director to verify that the previous day's shooting was satisfactory artistically and technically. These prints are termed the rushes. Meanwhile, the negative is carefully put to one side. Where there have been several takes of a scene, the director can save processing costs by asking the laboratory to print only those he wishes to see.

These rushes are joined together, to provide a cutting-copy—the film editor's preliminary arrangement and selection of the sequencies from the camera. This version is termed the rough cut. Finally, a more effectively edited fine-cut is produced, showing the film in its final form. By this time, the work print of film will probably suffer from scratches and dust accumulated in the cutting room. Now the original negative is cut by the laboratory to match the fine-cut print. Show-prints may then be made from this negative; although in certain organisations the negative itself is televised, and electronically reversed to provide a positive version.

Reversal film
In a reversal film process, the original film negative material is itself transformed into the positive print. All editing has therefore to be done on this master, though copies are possible by first making an inter-negative. Copies made by this method are not of comparable quality with those produced by negative-positive process. The advantages of reversal film (colour or black-and-white) are convenience, cheapness and speed of processing. It is, therefore, a method finding wide favour for news gathering, particularly when the film has a combined sound track. The limitations of reversal film are generally considered a worthwhile sacrifice in these circumstances.

Colour systems
When shooting on colour negative stock, only about 10% of the cutting copy is actually printed in colour in order to conserve costs. Once the negative has been cut, a first answer print is made in colour, enabling the errors in density and colour balance to be assessed and corrected by the laboratory. Should these not prove satisfactory, different corrections are made in subsequent second (and possibly third) prints, until a suitable version is obtained. Repeating the finished treatment (printer-light settings), further similar show prints may then be obtained.

138

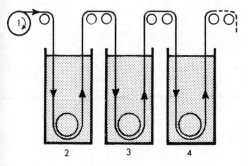
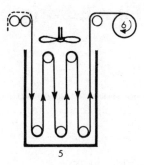

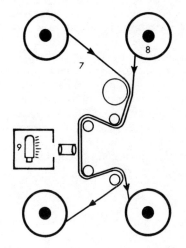

FILM PROCESSING

Basic film processing

The exposed film from the camera is *developed* to form a visible image (darkened in proportion to light in the original scene). After rinsing or stop baths (to stop chemical action) the *fixer* removes unwanted chemical materials (stabilising film to light). The resulting negative film is washed and dried. (Colour film requires certain additional stages.)

In a typical processor, film is fed from the exposed film magazine (1) through continuous motion processing baths (2), (3), (4), etc. to a drying cabinet (5) and take-up spool (6). The first cabinets are always totally enclosed and light-proof but after fixing, subsequent tanks need not be light-proof.

The film printer

To provide a positive copy (print), this negative (7) is run in contact with a roll of raw (unexposed) film stock (8) which is systematically exposed to a light source (9) through the negative.

This exposed film is subsequently processed as before, and a positive print (i.e. a negative of a negative) results.

139

Film Editing

Basically, the film editor is responsible for assembling in appropriate order and duration, the material shot by the director (usually out of sequence) and any inserts from selected library film (stock shots). Exactly how he chooses to juxtapose and interrelate this film, will directly influence its impact on the audience. Its entire meaning, its emphasis, its pace, can be modified by his treatment.

Editing room
Editing is clearly a skilled craft, and we can only outline here typical facilities that one can expect to find in the editing room. The room itself should be well ventilated and dust free. For optimum viewing conditions windows should be fitted with blinds and the room lighting intensity adjustable.

Throughout the editing process, the pictures and their associated sound recording are usually in the form of two separate films. These have to be run in synchronism, and to ensure this, special editing machines have evolved. The prime requirement of any film editing machine is for the operator to be able to view his film at any speed from 'still-frame' to 'fast speed' while hearing its related sound track, in order to decide precisely the order, duration, and cutting point for each shot. If the sound track is on another film as in sepmag (page 136), the editor can advance the picture or eliminate sections, in order to synchronise them.

Editing equipment
The simplest form of editing machine consists of a geared, hand-driven sprocket-wheel assembly that conveys the film under a magnifier backed by a rear-illuminated ground glass screen. Another sprocket-wheel carries the sound track past a sound head, the output of which may be amplified and heard on a loudspeaker. The film reels are held on simple supports (film horses). More sophisticated machines are motor driven at variable speeds, with larger projection-screens, and have fast wind and rewind facilities.

Hand-wound machines with additional sound-heads and sprocket-wheels to carry extra sound-tracks (e.g. dialogue, background effects, music tracks), are called synchronisers and are standard equipment in most cutting rooms.

Film jointing
Two systems for joining film are available. In the regular permanent method, a liquid cement is used to fuse the film together in a strong overlap joint. For speed and convenience however, temporary butt-joints can be made, held together with special transparent adhesive tape. If a tape-joined film is to be viewed on a projector, it is a wise precaution to join both sides of the film.

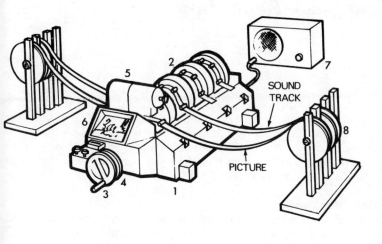

SOUND
TRACK

PICTURE

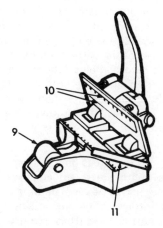

FILM EDITING EQUIPMENT
The synchroniser
This cutting room device (1) enables several lengths of film to be located in exact
synchronism. The revolving sprockets (2) are locked together on their common spindle
once sync has been obtained. From then on, rotation of the spindle by the handle (3),
the rim of which is calibrated in film frames (4) moves all the films simultaneously. A
lamp inside the housing (5) enables the film to be viewed on the ground glass screen
(6). The sound tracks can be monitored on the amplifier (7). The film is supported on
either side by film horses (8).

The tape joiner
This apparatus enables film to be joined (butt joint) with transparent adhesive tape (9).
Perforations may be punched-out after joining and trimming blades cut the tape (10).
Tape joins are essentially less permanent than film cement versions, but serve
particularly for editing preparation. The film may be trimmed with the knife (11).

141

Video Tape Recording

From the early days of television, engineers attempted to devise techniques for recording pictures and sound simultaneously on magnetic tape. Audio frequencies span about ten octaves—about the limit of tape recording technology, so a method had to be devised to compress the vision signal to encompass no more than this. The technique universally employed is to frequency-modulate the vision signal, to produce lower-sideband excursions that fall within the recorder's range. To reproduce this, the head gap-width must be small, and the effective head-tape speed high.

VT Recorder Design

In the first commercially successful design four heads are used, mounted at right angles on a revolving drum which scans two inch wide tape laterally at 250 rps. The tape is transported across the drum at $15\frac{5}{8}$ inches per second (European standards). Vision tracks are thus recorded across the tape. By this means an effective writing speed of 1580 ips is achieved. Each track contains some 16 lines of picture information. An electronic switch is employed on replay to switch between the successive tracks at the correct moment.

The sound information is recorded along the top of the tape, and cue and control tracks are recorded along the bottom of the tape. The control track is used to control the capstan speed on replay.

Quadrature machines, as they are known, are still the main professional means of video recording used throughout the world.

Helical scan recorders

In recent years another format known as helical scan has become widely used (page 144). This technique again employs a rotating head assembly but uses only one or two heads. The tape is wound in a helix around the drum. Thus each frame of the vision signal is recorded as a shallow diagonal track along the tape. They are usually portable, and easier to operate and maintain than quadrature machines.

Identification clock

One method of ensuring that each video recording is fully labelled, is to preface the recording with an 'identification clock'. The clock is started by the floor manager one minute before the action commences. A typical routine is: standard 1kHz. tone from −20 to −10 secs., a verbal countdown second by second from −10 to −3 secs., then silence as the studio is faded out from −3 to 0 secs.

Storage

Tapes should be stored upright and away from magnetic fields, in a clean room that is not subject to large temperature or humidity changes. Cataloguing is essential and periodic reviews of the store to recycle tape used for redundant recordings reduces tape costs.

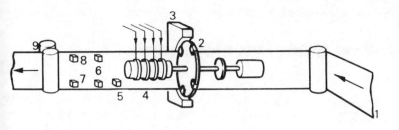

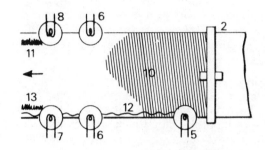

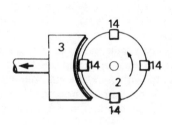

VIDEOTAPE RECORDING

Tape transport and head layout

The magnetically neutral 2 in. wide tape (1) driven by the capstan and pressure rollers (9), passes the speed-controlled head-drum (2). Here a vacuum guide (3) ensures accurate close tape contact. Video in the form of frequency-modulated signals is fed to head-drum via slip rings or rotary transformers. The control track (5) records the 250 Hz stabiliser-drum motor speed. Erase heads (6) demagnetise sound and cue tracks for recording at (7), (8) respectively.

The frequency-modulated signal (carrying the video) is recorded as a series of narrow stripes across the tape (10). The sound track is continuously recorded along the upper tape edge (11); while along the lower edge a control track (12) and a cue track (13) (a second sound track) are located.

Quadrature recording – the head drum

Quadrature recording uses four magnetic heads (14) mounted within a rotating drum (2), to both record and reproduce the composite video signal on the tape.

Identification clock

The clock contains all identification for the programme recording, and helps to cue the start of videotape reproduction.

143

Helical Scan Developments

The development of helical scan recorders was the first successful design departure from conventional quadrature videotape machines. Development has been rapid, but unfortunately there has been no standardisation between manufacturers. As a result machines are available catering for widely differing markets and employing totally different recording standards. As well as reel-to-reel machines, easy to operate cassette and cartridge recorders are now available within the pocket of the domestic consumer. Some machines can record from, and replay through an ordinary television receiver.

Typical design
The usual video recording technique is to employ one or two heads mounted on a head drum (as in quadrature machines, page 142) which revolves in the plane of the tape transport. The tape, which may be of various widths from ¼-in. to 2 in., is transported around the drum between spools at different levels so that the head traces a shallow diagonal track along the tape. There are two methods of wrapping the tape around the head drum; described by their appearance, as alpha and omega wraps. Sound, erase and control-track heads are static heads, as with quadrature machines. Each video track contains one frame of information, so that, with some machines, a still frame is possible by simply not advancing the tape and continuously repeating one frame of information. Electronic editing is possible with most helical machines (page 146). Physical editing (i.e. cutting the tape) is not practicable, because the cut would sever many tracks, so producing a disturbance to the reproduced picture.

Colour reproduction
The principal difficulty with helical machines lies in the mechanical limitations of the tape and its transport. Phase and timing errors throughout each track can be considerable (causing hue and other discrepancies) and for this reason development has been directed mainly toward the audio-visual and industrial markets. Various ingenious methods of deriving colour playbacks from helical recorders have been devised. Many machines provide acceptable colour pictures for closed circuit viewing though not within broadcast tolerances. Nevertheless, broadcast-quality videotape recorders which combine the advantages of quadrature and helical recorders have been designed. Their sophisticated electronics render them expensive by comparison with other helical machines but their performance is claimed to be as good as, even superior to current quadrature machines and at a competitive price. As this is an innovation in professional recorder design, facilities can be incorporated that are not possible on existing equipment: e.g. two good-quality audio tracks, and an address (time) code track to enhance editing techniques (page 146).

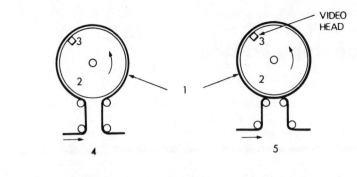

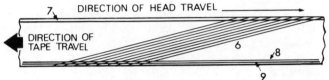

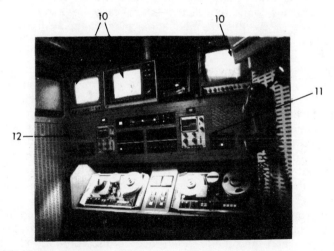

VIDEOTAPE
Helical scan type wraps
The magnetic tape (1) winds round a large diameter drum (2) in a helical configuration. A video head (3) protrudes through a slot in this hollow drum revolving at a constant speed. The tape moves relatively slowly, and is scanned rapidly by the head. The two most common head-wrap arrangements are known as alpha (4) and omega (5).

Typical helical scan tape format
The video is recorded as slantwise diagonal tracks (6), the full width of the tape. However video information is lost as the head leaves the tape after each track. This *crossover* disturbance usually occurs during frame blanking period. Some machines include a *processor* reinserting syncs during this period. Audio track (7) runs along one edge, control track (8) and cue track (9) along the other.

A comprehensive helical-scan videotape area
Two machines facilitate continuous recording. Picture monitor screens (10), waveform monitors (11) and monitor loudspeakers (12) provide continuous checks of video and audio quality.

Videotape Editing

Before the advent of electronic editing the only method of editing videotape was to cut and butt-join the tape. Difficulties arise owing to the displacement of the sound track from the corresponding vision (9¼in./0·6 sec.). Simple edits may be made where a fade-out and fade-in occur, i.e. where black level and silence occur. More complicated edits are possible, using a separate audio tape recorder to dub off the sound, but these can be very time consuming. Helical scan recordings cannot be cut-edited without vision disturbance because the cut would sever many video tracks. A long diagonal cut is not practicable.

Electronic editing
Cut-editing has gradually been superseded by electronic editing. Now available on most new machines (quadrature and helical) it leaves the tape mechanically sound (physical cuts limit tape-life) and permits unlimited revisions. By this method a machine in replay immediately switches to record, on operation of a button, with no interruption to the picture or sound.

Some videotape recorders can be remote controlled so that editing can be carried out from the production control room, thus reducing post editing time — important where demands on machine-time are high. With this facility, the director can watch a playback of the previously-recorded sequence and then cue the performers just before the edit is to be carried out. More sophisticated machines permit the director to rehearse his edit until he is satisfied with its timing. An audible cue-tone is heard over loudspeakers in the studio and the control room in advance of the edit point (1·2 seconds on quadrature machines). The floor manager can then cue action before the edit occurs.

Where programmes are not completed in the studio, editing may be carried out using two sets of machines; one (or more) to playback (replay) tapes, and the other a video-recorder incorporating electronic editing facilities. Sound dubbing of music and sound effects is often carried out after the videotape has been edited (post-edit dubbing).

Time Code Numbering
As machine (and operator) time is expensive, a means has been devised of magnetically recording on the cue-track a digital 'time-code', numbering every frame of the TV picture. A copy (dubbing) is made on a helical scan recorder with this time-code information added to the picture by means of a video character generator. The director takes the helical-scan recorder to his office and, viewing the programme at his leisure, notes the time-code reading precisely where he decides each cut should occur. The videotape editor then cuts the master tape at these time-code readings thus achieving a substantial saving on the quadrature machine (and operator time).

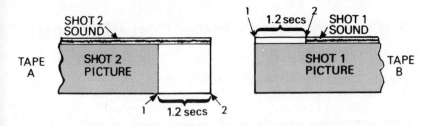

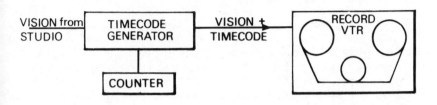

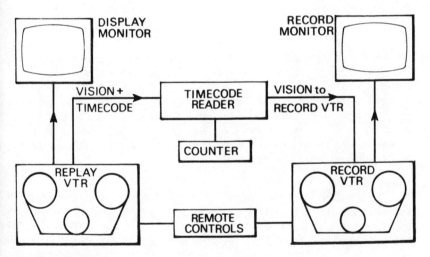

EDITING VIDEOTAPE
Physical editing
Physical cuts on helical systems are never completely satisfactory, as splices cannot be made between the slanting traoks. A right-angles cut produces a vertical wipe.

Because the sound and vision tracks are displaced on quadrature recordings, a cut in tape A at (1) introduces a 1.2 sec. loss of "Shot 2" sound; or a cut at (2) adds 1.2 secs. of spurious picture or blank tape (black level).

In tape B, a cut at (1) results in 1.2 secs. spurious sound (or silence); while a cut at (2) loses 1.2 secs. of the "Shot 1" picture.

Electronic editing – time code
During recording (or dubbing), time-code information in binery form may be recorded on the cue track identifying every electronic frame for subsequent editing.

During replay, this cue track information is detected and read out on a counter indicator. Editing points can be chosen with precision, using this identification.

147

Programme and Production Planning

In the smallest studios, one can often get by on an *ad hoc* basis, but as the studio centre acquires more facilities (and staff), some form of advance planning control is needed. Planning takes two distinct forms: the overall planning and allocation of station facilities, and the planning of individual studio productions.

Need to co-ordinate

Systems (programme) planning co-ordinates projected studio productions, and broadly estimates the staff, facilities and, in some cases, the financial arrangements, required to stage these programmes. In a larger studio complex this includes co-ordination of the equipment and installation maintenance requirements, staging and lighting schedules, the use of ancillary technical facilities (telecine, videotape, filming facilities, etc.) and staff availability.

Production planning

Production planning is concerned with the mounting of individual studio programmes. This is the translation of a script into the staffing requirements, equipment and facilities needed to mount that programme. Production planning is initiated by a meeting between the director and his team, including specialists concerned with staging, lighting, technical operations (cameras, sound), costume, make-up, etc. The director indicates his aims, and the team discusses the requirements and logistics involved, before organising their own particular contributions. The time-scale varies, of course, with the complexity and nature of the production.

Floor plan

The floor plan that details proposed staging layouts is a scale plan of the studio with details of its facilities; usually to a scale of 1:50. This plan indicates the available staging area, squared in units of half a metre; small crosses indicate the intersection of the overhead lighting grid. On a copy of this floor plan (ground plan) the designer details all scenic outlines (a further set of drawings shows elevations of all staging). Once agreed by the team, he activates staging operations, while the production director uses a copy for his detailed planning of action and camera treatment. Using a protractor set to the camera lens' horizontal angle, he checks the exact picture content for each camera's position. Thus the floor plan becomes a blueprint for a particular show. As well as details of furnishings, cameras, sound booms, and any other operational equipment are subsequently marked on the plan. Lighting treatment, too, is devised, based on this staging plan, showing the positions of all lamps and associated requirements. Subsequently, this lighting plot becomes the guide-line for all lighting rigging, and control of lighting treatment for the production.

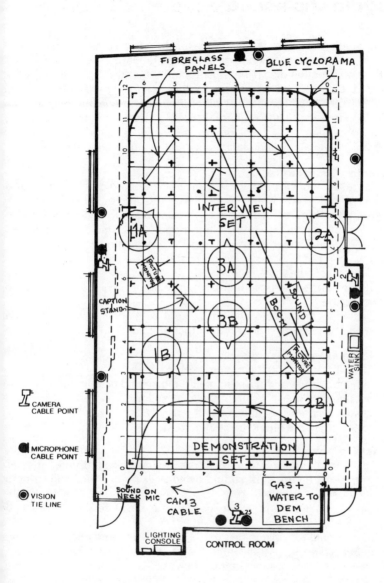

FIBREGLASS PANELS

BLUE CYCLORAMA

INTERVIEW SET

1A

2A

3A

PICTURE MONITOR

CAPTION STAND

SOUND BOOM

3B

PICTURE MONITOR

1B

WATER SINK

2B

DEMONSTRATION SET

$\mathcal{I}$ CAMERA CABLE POINT

MICROPHONE CABLE POINT

VISION TIE LINE

SOUND ON NECK MIC

CAM 3 CABLE

GAS + WATER TO DEM BENCH

3 25

LIGHTING CONSOLE

CONTROL ROOM

STUDIO FLOOR PLAN

The studio floor plan shows the disposition of all technical facilities in the studio. Scenery is drawn on this plan, together with furniture. Subsequently camera and sound boom positions are indicated. Thus the plan serves as a valuable communications document. Cameras' positions shown as 1A, 1B. 2A, 2B. 3A, 3B.

149

Studio Discipline

Good studio discipline is necessary for the effective use of the studio and the maintenance of good programme standards.

First, production discipline: it is essential that the programme is well planned. Don't wait until the studio day to sort out your ideas. Studio time is expensive! There must be one person in overall control of the studio operations — the director. All staff must keep to the timetable of studio operations, i.e. meal breaks, rehearsal periods, studio line-up recording time, etc. Good planning should result in few over-runs.

Avoiding disturbance
1. There should be strict observance of the studio condition, i.e. or rehearsal, the need for absolute quiet in the studio and minimum staff interruption in the control rooms. On transmission (and recording), the need for absolute quiet and no interruption of any studio operations.
2. Staff should be disciplined not to touch studio props, caption stands, sound mixing desks, vision mixing desks, lighting consoles, etc. which may have been carefully set up at rehearsals.
3. Studio staff should avoid crossing the actors' eyeline — this can be very distracting.
4. Visitors to the studio should be kept to a minimum, should keep quiet, and be permitted only under strict guidance.

Avoiding extraneous noise
1. All studio staff should wear soft-soled shoes.
2. All headphones not in use in the studio should be unplugged, to prevent inadvertent mic. pick-up of talkback sound.
3. All studio doors should be closed properly.
4. No talking in the studio (except actors).

General precautions
To ensure minimum frustrations to the engineering staff when they are lining up the camera, staff should avoid walking between the cameras and their line-up charts.

Access to fire exits must be kept clear. Fire lanes must be unobstructed.

There should be no smoking in the studio itself, except for the actors if required to do so. At all times the studio should be kept as tidy as possible — no newspapers in the studio, old scripts disposed of properly, no cups/saucers on monitors, loudspeakers, boom platforms.

Equipment care
At the end of the production, time should be allocated for the proper derigging of equipment. Finally, a reminder of the importance of allocating regular maintenance periods. Faulty equipment should be investigated and repaired as soon as possible — even if spare equipment is available.

150

STUDIO DISCIPLINE

Studio warning indicators

Prominent indicators should show clearly whether a rehearsal or a recording/transmission is in progress. Indicator lights too, both inside and outside entrances ensure full coverage. (Blue for rehearsal conditions; red lamps, flashing, for recording/transmission.) Protective frames prevent accidental damage.

How to be helpful

Studio discipline is a matter of anticipation and consideration for others. Here we list a few typical hazards for the unwary. Remember, you may be the victim of somebody else's carelessness!

Avoid getting into shot.

Do not chat during studio rehearsals.

Avoid casting shadows in shot.

Wear soft-soled shoes.

Don't smoke in the studio.

Don't touch other people's equipment, properties, etc.

Avoid disturbing cables, floor lamps, etc.

Don't leave debris around (coffee cups, scripts, etc.) especially on equipment.

Unplug headsets when not in use (to avoid accidental pick-up of talkback speech).

Do not stand in front of picture monitors or foldback loudspeakers.

Keep off a performer's eyeline (odd movements and reactions can distract).

Arrangements vary, but the principles are universal.

Staffing and Responsibilities

The staffing requirements for a small television studio depend on the type of productions and the scale of the operations involved. It is not generally possible to have separate specialists to the same extent as a large studio complex. Many staff need to have a flexible approach, developing expertise in several jobs, to reduce the problems of sickness and holiday reliefs on a small station.

The specialised techniques of television production, engineering and technical operations are not acquired overnight. It is recommended that staff are recruited who have the necessary specialised knowledge and experience or, at the junior levels, staff are recruited with potential and given correct formal training.

Studio Crew

The duties of the production team can be summarised as follows:

Director: In overall control; he is responsible for realising the programme within the specified time schedule. His work includes the direction of the technical crew, vision mixer and the artists.

Producer's assistant: In the studio she assists the director by calling 'shot' numbers on a scripted programme, cueing facilities and timing of programme items.

Vision mixer (switcher): Operates the vision mixing panel. Often on small productions the director may do this himself.

Floor manager: The director's link man on the studio floor. He relays instructions to the artists, and is responsible for good studio floor discipline.

Technical director: Responsible for the technical and artistic quality of the studio output. He heads the operational crew, and may be directly concerned with productional lighting. (On small-budget studios he may also operate the lighting console.)

Vision control: Responsible for the operation of the lighting console and the pictorial matching of picture sources.

Senior cameraman: Responsible for his camera crew's work, including the training of new staff.

Cameramen: Operation of studio cameras.

Camera assistants: Assist on the studio floor with cameras, cables, rigging of the cameras, monitors, etc.

Sound control: Responsible for all aspects of the production's sound coverage. This includes the operation of the sound mixing desk, placing of microphones, supervising and training of sound assistants.

Sound assistants: Rigging of sound equipment, operating microphone booms, operating audio-tape and gram machines.

Telecine operator: To operate (and maintain) telecine machine.

Videotape operator: To operate videotape equipment.

Studio engineers: Alignment and maintenance of the technical facilities in the studio.

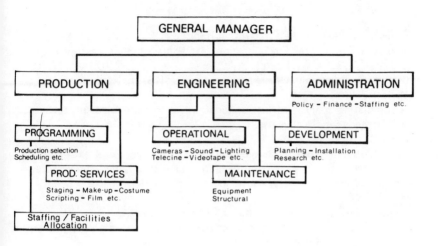

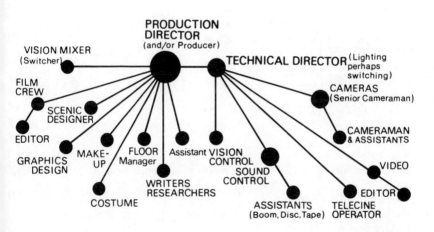

STUDIO ADMINISTRATION
Organisation
The organisation of even the smallest studio complex, requires the co-ordinated skills of many different professions. Even this very broad outline hints at the diversity involved.

The production team
The Production Director co-ordinates the work of a team of specialists. Together they decide the artistic parameters of the show, and organise the various services involved in production mechanics.

Further Reading

COMBES, PETER & TIFFIN, JOHN:
Television Production for Education (1st edn.) 1978 Focal Press, London.
GORDON, GEORGE:
Classroom Television: New Frontiers in ITV (1970), Hastings House, New York.
A stimulating analysis of instructional TV, covering equipment, technology and methods for effective use.
HAPPE, BERNARD:
Basic Motion Picture Technology. (2nd edn.) 1975 Focal Press, London.
A comprehensive survey of the technique of film; a non technical approach for production executives, creative artists and technicians alike.
HOLM, W.A.:
Colour Television Explained. Philips Technical Library.
Examines the theoretical bases of colour television and the problems arising out of its practical realisation.
JONES, PETER:
The Technique of the Television Cameraman. (3rd edn.) 1972 Focal Press, London.
A book primarily intended for a newcomer to the field, it is a comprehensive guide to the work of the TV cameraman.
KINROSS, FELICITY:
Television for the Teacher (1968) Hamish Hamilton, London.
A well illustrated guide for the teacher on the use of television as a visual aid to teaching.
MILLERSON, GERALD:
The Technique of Television Production. (10th edn.) 1979 Focal Press, London.
A comprehensive survey of the mechanics, art, methods and techniques used in television studio work. A practical reference work of encyclopaedic scope.
MILLERSON, Gerald:
The Technique of Lighting for Television and Motion Pictures (2nd edn.) 1982. Focal Press, London.
A book offering a deep and comprehensive study of both the art and the technique of creative lighting for TV and motion pictures, from basic principles through the sophisticated and specialised applications.
MOIR, GUTHRIE:
Teaching and Television (TV Explained) (1967). Pergamon Press, Oxford, PP inc, New York.
The application of educational television at all levels explained for educationalists.

NISBETT, ALEC:
The Technique of the Sound Studio. (4th edn.) 1979 Focal Press, London.
An authoritative reference book for all who work with sound in television, radio, recording studio and film.

NISBETT, ALEC:
The Use of Microphones. (2nd edn.) 1983. Focal Press, London.
A compact volume covering microphones and related equipment. Recommended for those primarily interested in sound balance.

WILKIE, BERNARD:
The Technique of Special Effects in Television. (1st edn.) 1971 Focal Press, London.
An interesting exploration into the world of television special effects.

YORKE, IVOR:
The Technique of Television News. (1st edn.) 1978 Focal Press, London.

Glossary

Amplitude Modulation A method of transmitting information, by changing the amplitude (strength) of a high frequency (carrier) wave in proportion to the amplitude of the lower frequency signal we wish to transmit. The amplitude-modulated carrier is subsequently detected (demodulated) and the original lower frequency signal recovered.

Aspect Ratio (82) The ratio between the horizontal and vertical lengths of the television picture frame. This is 4:3 for all television systems.

Attenuator A resistance network introduced into a circuit, which enables the amplitude of a signal to be reduced without creating distortion.

Audio Oscillator Apparatus which generates sinusoidal oscillations at frequencies in the audio waveband.

Aural Sensitivity Network A filter which 'has the characteristics of the human ear' (a precise definition has yet to be internationally agreed).

Backlight (92) Light from behind the subject, providing tonal separation between this subject and its background. Backlight also reveals contours and edge-texture. A hard source is normally used for these purposes.

Bandwidth (142) The range of frequencies encompassed by an electronic system transmitting television pictures (video), or sound (audio) signals. A video system must be capable of handling a wide frequency range (wide bandwidth) if it is to transmit pictures with fine detail.

Barn Doors (92) Four flaps fitted to a spotlight which are used to control the shape of the light beam.

Black Edge (72) Facility for electronically creating a thin black edge around light overlayed lettering to improve legibility against backgrounds of similar tone.

Blimp A sound-absorbent cover made to cut down to acceptable limits the noise generated by mechanical equipment (notably film cameras).

Camera Angle (148) A general term for the line the camera makes with the subject it is shooting. Hence high angle, low angle shots.

Caption Scanner Apparatus for televising 35mm transparencies or small (12″ by 9″) graphics. It may incorporate a scanning tube (flying-spot scanner) or a camera tube (e.g. vidicon).

Cardioid Microphone (102) Microphone whose directivity pattern (polar diagram) is heart-shaped, resulting in maximum sensitivity at the front and very low sensitivity at the rear.

Channel (110, 54, 90) A general term for a succession of apparatus having a combined function. In a sound mixing desk, for example, a section handling the output of one audio source (e.g. microphone – amplifiers – fader – filtering, etc.,) as opposed to a group of sources.

A vision channel embraces the complete video generating system for a single picture source (e.g. camera – amplifiers – associated supplies and scanning systems – switching circuits – distribution amplifier, etc.).

A lighting channel is the complete lighting circuit supplying a particular luminaire (e.g. power routing – switching – patching – dimmer – plugging, etc.).

Character Generator (74) Electronic generation of lettering or numbers, for display on a TV screen. The generator's output appears on the vision mixing desk as a standard picture source, or on the studio output, and is controlled from a form of typewriter keyboard.

Clean Feed (110) (111) An output from a sound desk which deliberately omits certain sources which are present in the total studio output. Clean Feeds are used in, for example, two-way working between studios to prevent acoustic howl round.

Coder (12) Circuitry for encoding the three separate red, green and blue components of a colour picture to produce a single composite signal. Whereas the original separate R.G.B. signals required three individual transmission channels, the encoded signal may be transmitted over a single line (cable or radio) and decoded to recover the separate components at the receiving point.

Cold Light Illuminator (38) An evenly illuminated ground glass screen used for lighting test transparencies. Cold cathode vapour tubes provide diffuse illumination without heat.

Colour Temperature (13) A term used to describe the colour quality of illumination from a light source. It is measured in kelvins (K). (0 K = $-273°C$).

Contrast (43) In pictures a comparison between the luminance of light and dark tones (tonal contrast), or relative lighting intensities (lighting contrast).

Control Line (134) A sound line or telephone circuit used for communication (talkback, private wire,) between a control room and a remote source.

Crab (46) The sideways movement of a television camera mounting, across a setting and parallel with it.

Cue Light A small light mounted on a floor or table stand in the studio, that is switched on from the control room in order to cue an artist.

Cut (70) An instantaneous change from one picture to another.

Cyclorama Cloth (Cyc) (30) A taut vertical cloth used as a scenic background.

dB (Decibel) (22, 108) Unit comparing electrical ratios e.g. n dB = 10 $\log_{10}$ (ratios of 2 powers). Voltage ratios are calculated from 20 $\log_{10}$

(ratio of 2 voltages). When dealing with audio signal levels it is usual to infer that the reference is ZERO LEVEL.

dB (A) (22) Unit of sound level; approximating to loudness. The reference level is 0·00002 Newtons/metre² (approximately the threshold of hearing at 1 kHz).

Decoder (12) Circuitry for retrieving the individual Red, Green, Blue colour signals from a coded colour video signal.

Depress (46) To lower a camera height (on a pedestal mounting, by reducing the column height).

Depth of Field (85) The distance between the nearest and farthest point from a camera that are within acceptable focus. Depth of field varies with lens aperture (stop), focused distance, and the focal length of the lens.

Dichroic Mirror (12) A surface-coated glass filter which permits certain parts of the visible spectrum to pass through while reflecting others. Used in colour television cameras and telecine systems to analyse the full-colour scene into R.G.B. components. A form of dichroic filter is used as a heat filter in projector systems to protect the film material from infra-red and heat rays.

Dimmer (96) An electrical device for controlling the light output from a luminaire (light fitting).

Directivity Pattern (102) A graphical plot representing the relative performance of a device at different distances and in various directions. It can show the sensitivity variations, or changes in frequency response of a microphone. Similarly it can demonstrate the way in which the output of a device (e.g. a lamp, or a loudspeaker) alters with angle and with distance.

Director (152) The person responsible for the organisation, creative interpretation and presentation of a particular programme. The functions of a director vary somewhat from one organisation to another.

Downstage (135) The activity area nearest to the camera. To walk 'downstage' means to walk towards the cameras.

Dynamic Range (114) In sound, the range of sound levels which the audio system can handle. At the top end of the scale it is limited by overload distortion and at the lower end by signal-to-noise considerations.

Echo (118) Strictly, a repetition of a sound due to the acoustical reflection from some obstacle. The term is used widely but strictly incorrectly to mean REVERBERATION.

Electrostatic Microphone (100) Microphone in which the conducting diaphragm upon which the sound impinges forms one plate of a

158

capacitor. Capacitance changes caused by diaphragm movements are converted into an output voltage.

Elevate (46) To raise camera height.

Exposure Meter (38) This measures either the intensity of incident light falling on the subject, or the amount of light reflected from a scene, in order to assess the camera operating conditions required to achieve 'correct exposure'. (In TV, the lens-aperture setting. In Film the lens-aperture and exposure time.)

Fader (68, 98, 108) General term for an intensity control, adjusting the strength of a signal. A fader may be used as a 'switch' to introduce/remove sources to the main output (hence 'fade up', 'fade down'). It may also be set at intermediate positions to adjust the relative outp)uts of sources (balance). Typical fader applications include vision and sound mixing consoles, and lighting control consoles.

Figure-of-eight (102) Type of microphone directivity pattern (so called from its polar diagram shape). The true three-dimensional pattern would be two spheres in contact, with the microphone at the point of contact.

Filler (92) Light (usually diffused — i.e. 'soft') used to control the lighting contrast, and to illuminate shadow areas cast by keylights.

Fish-pole (104) Simple hand-held microphone boom. It consists of about 2 m of suitable rod with a mounting at one end to support the microphone.

Flat (28) A basic scenic unit. Usually made of stretched canvas or hardboard on a flat wooden framework.

Floor Manager (152) The person responsible for the productional organisation (including performer cueing) and general discipline in the studio. He is the Director's representative on the floor.

Floor Plan (20, 148) Scale plan of the studio floor area, usually to a scale of 1:50.

F Numbers (44) A set of numbers engraved on the body of a lens adjacent to the iris setting showing relative apertures. (Obtained by dividing the focal length by the effective diameter of the iris.) All lenses at the same f. No. should give the same exposure (assuming identical transmission factors).

Fold Back (F/B) (108, 110) The reproduction of selected sound sources over studio loudspeakers as an aid to performers (e.g. fold back of disc sound effects).

Frequency Modulation (142) A method of transmitting information by changing the frequency of a high frequency carrier wave in proportion to the amplitude of the lower frequency signal we wish to transmit. (The amplitude of the carrier remains unchanged.) The frequency-modulated carrier is subsequently demodulated to recover the original signal.

Group (108) In a sound desk two or more channels may be faded up together, and so combined into a group. A single group fader then controls all these sources simultaneously.

Gun Microphone (102) Type of microphone with an extremely narrow pick-up angle, making it particularly useful for isolating individual sound sources, and for long-distance operations. Such microphones embody a slotted or perforated tube, typically about 0.5 m long

Hard Source Any light source which produces sharply defined shadows. The more compact a light source is (i.e. the nearer it approaches a point source) the more clear-cut will be the shadows, modelling, and texture produced by it.

Harmonic An oscillatory motion (mechanical or electrical) that is a multiple of a fundamental frequency.

Harmonic distortion Changes in the total harmonic content in a signal caused by non-linear circuits.

Head Gap (142) The magnetic gap between the poles in tape recorder heads.

Hertz (Hz) The unit of frequency (cycles-per-second). The number of complete oscillatory vibrations or excursions per second.

Inter-negative (138) **(Dupe negative).** A negative derived from a print (positive), enabling further prints (dupe prints) to be produced.

Illumination (43, 85) A measure of the amount of light incident on a surface. It is measured in LUX (lumens/m²) or foot-candles (lumens/ft²).

Keylight (92) This is the main light source illuminating the subject. It establishes the shape of the subject, revealing modelling and texture. The keylight can suggest the direction of an inferred light source. Hard light sources (fresnel spotlights) are normally used as keylights.

Lift (56) An electronic adjustment in a camera or telecine channel (usually operated continuously for optimum picture equality), which moves all picture tones up or down the tonal scale. This is achieved by adjusting the video signal's d.c. level relative to picture black level.

Limiter/Compressor (108, 114) Electronic device for automatic control of sound programme levels; often used to prevent signals exceeding system parameters.

Linear Source (92) A tungsten-halogen strip light. (Typically 119 mm long and 13 mm in diameter.) Used in soft-light sources and cyc lights.

Luminaire (92, 93) The term used to describe a complete light unit i.e. housing and bulb. The general term *lamp* is widely used instead, although it strictly denotes the actual light source (i.e. the bulb or envelope, and its filament).

Luminance (61) A measure of the amount of light which is *reflected* from a surface. It is measured in APOSTILB's (lumens/m²) or FOOT LAMBERT's (lumens/ft²).

Lux (85) The practical metric unit of illumination.

Mix (70) The progressive fading out of one source and the fading up of a second. In vision, the first picture merges into the second.

Modulator (64) An electronic facility used when television signals are to be distributed by coaxial cable over an appreciable distance, or made available at a number of monitoring points throughout an area. By superimposing the picture and sound signals on a radio frequency carrier, high quality results are achievable, viewed on conventional TV receivers.

Monitor (58, 74) A mute television display unit in general use in studio centres. Monitors may show individual outputs of cameras, telecine, VTR, etc., or the integrated (switched) output from a studio or network. The monitor is invariably line-fed by a coaxial cable (no aerial connection) and has no audio output or loudspeaker.

Munsell System (28) A system of colour notation, classifying a wide range of hues at varying degrees of saturation. The luminance of a surface is scaled in values from 10 (White) to 0 (Black). Surfaces with the same luminance value will appear the same tone (shade of grey) on a monochrome display.

Music Circuit (programme line) A high-grade sound line, permitting wide-band low distortion transmission of audio signals; particularly between a remote source and its destination.

Overlay (72) An electronic switch enabling the pictures from two television sources to be integrated. A subject is placed front of a special 'keying' tone or hue (not present in the subject itself). The overlay switch automatically substitutes for the key colour, a chosen background scene (from another television camera, telecine, videotape, etc.).

Patch Panel (90) A system for connecting luminaires distributed about the studio with a selected series of supply circuits (usually incorporating dimmers/switching/protection devices). It frequently takes the form of a plug and socket (jackfield) arrangement.

Pan (46) Swivel the camera head left or right on its support mounting (panning head).

Pantograph (88) A spring-counterbalanced, collapsible, lighting suspension unit designed on the lazy-tongs principle. Units are available which allow the heights of luminaire of various weights to be adjusted easily over a wide range.

Peak Programme Meter (PPM) (112) Meter for indicating peaks of sound levels, thus enabling an operator to avoid overmodulation distortions, etc.

Perspective (Sound) (126) The illusion of distance of a sound source.

Perspective (Vision) In pictorial terms, an illusion of depth and space created by the use of decor, lighting and lens-angle selection. It is essential for picture and sound to maintain related perspective to create a co-ordinated effect.

Phantom powering (101) A method of supplying power to electro-static microphones along the 3-cored cable used for the audio signal

Phase Distortion Distortion arising when the relative phases of component parts of a complex wave are changed.

Presence Filter (108, 116) Circuit boosting a region of the frequency response of a sound channel. It can often convey the impression that certain sound source stands out from its background.

Producer (152) The person responsible for the overall planning financial control and artistic shape of a series of programes.

Profile Projector (94) An alternative name for a hard edged projector

Public Address (P.A.) (110) In television studio operations, a feed of selected sources being reproduced by loudspeakers near a studio audience.

Raster (60) The bright rectangular area formed on the screen of a television picture tube (by an unmodulated scanning beam tracking an interlaced line pattern on its phosphor surface).

Receiver (74) Electronic equipment which converts electric waves or currents received from an aerial system into a perceptible form — displayed picture and/or audible programme.

Reverberation (24) The prolongation of sound caused by repeated reflections from walls, floor, ceiling etc.

Reverberation Time (24) The time taken for the reverberant sound to decay through 60 dB.

Script Rehearsal script only contains the actors lines (dialogue) and basic action (moves). A *camera script* also includes the operational technical and staging information required for production treatment.

Shot An uninterrupted picture from one camera.

Sidebands (142) The band of frequencies either side of a carrier frequency, resulting from the process of modulation.

Soft Source (92) A light source (preferably of large area) which produces diffused illumination, and hence soft edged shadows.

Target (42) The part of the television pick-up tube where the electron image is formed. By varying the voltage applied to the target, the amplitude (strength) of the picture signal in a vidicon tube can be adjusted.

Termination (60) The electrical load value required to match the output impedance of a piece of equipment, or a line.

Tie-line (134) Interlinking sound or vision connection routed between technical areas.

Tilt (46) To tip the camera head upwards or downwards, on its panning-head.

Transducer: (119) A device for converting one type of energy into another, e.g. loudspeaker converts electrical signals to sound waves.

Trimming Tool A tool made of non-magnetic material used for adjusting the position of ferric cores inside coils (i.e. tuning them).

Upstage (135) The acting area farthest away from the camera. Hence to walk 'upstage' is to walk away from the camera.

Vision Mixer (68) A control panel or console enabling picture sources (cameras, telecine, caption, scanners, etc.,) to be selected individually or in groups, by switches or faders. Also the term for a specialist operator (switcher) of the apparatus.

Windshield (100) A gauze or fabric shield fitted over a microphone to reduce the audible effects of wind, breath etc., (i.e. plops).

Xenon Lamp A discharge type projection lamp having a colour temperature of about 6500°K (the standard for projecting colour film).

Zero Level (113) In audio engineering, a signal equivalent to a sine wave of r.m.s. value 0·775 V. (The voltage developed across a resistance of 600 Ω when 1 mW is dissipated in it.)

Zoom Lens (44) A lens system having moveable elements, so providing continuously variable focal length, and hence adjustable angle of view. A zoom lens may be set to any lens-angle within its range (e.g. 5° to 50°); or adjusted while on shot to produce varying magnification of the subject (zooming).